Better Homes and Gardens®

CHRISTMAS

FROM THE HEART

Volume 21

Meredith® Consumer Marketing
Des Moines, Iowa

Better Homes and Gardens.

CHRISTMAS
FROM THE HEART

Meredith Corporation Consumer Marketing
Senior Vice President, Consumer Marketing: Janet Donnelly
Consumer Product Marketing Director: Steve Swanson
Consumer Product Marketing Manager: Wendy Merical
Senior Production Manager: Steve Krider
Business Director: Ron Clingman
Photographers: Scott Little, Kritsada Panichgul, Jay Wilde

Waterbury Publications, Inc.
Contributing Editor: Carol Field Dahlstrom
Contributing Graphic Designer: Bruce Yang
Contributing Illustrator: Chris Neubauer Graphics
Contributing Food Editor: Lois White
Contributing Food Stylists: Charles Worthington, Jennifer Peterson
Contributing Copy Editor: Terri Fredrickson
Contributing Proofreader: Gretchen Kauffman

Editorial Director: Lisa Kingsley
Creative Director: Ken Carlson
Associate Editors: Tricia Bergman, Mary Williams
Associate Design Directors: Doug Samuelson, Todd Hanson
Production Assistant: Mindy Samuelson

Better Homes and Gardens **Magazine**
Editor in Chief: Gayle Goodson Butler
Art Director: Michael D. Belknap
Deputy Editor, Food and Entertaining: Nancy Wall Hopkins
Senior Food Editor: Richard Swearinger
Associate Food Editor: Erin Simpson
Editorial Assistant: Renee Irey

Meredith Publishing Group
President: Tom Harty

Meredith Corporation
Chairman and Chief Executive Officer: Stephen M. Lacy

In Memoriam: E.T. Meredith III (1933–2003)

All of us at Meredith Consumer Marketing are dedicated to providing you with information and ideas to enhance your home. We welcome your comments and suggestions. Write to us at: Meredith Consumer Marketing, 1716 Locust St., Des Moines, IA 50309-3023.

contents

CHIRSTMAS IS IN THE AIR—we are taking walks in the sparkling snow, cuddling up with a cup of hot cocoa, singing Christmas carols, and wrapping gifts as we watch favorite holiday movies. We are planning parties with friends and anticipating family to arrive back home. Because we know how much you love Christmas, we have filled this book with everything you need to make it a holiday filled with memories. You'll find stockings to sew, hats to knit, greeting cards to construct, and ornaments to paint. There are soft felted wreaths, beaded bracelets, quilted pot holders, carved candles, and tiny needle-felted reindeer. And you'll love the chapter on Christmas comfort food—soups, breads, and from-the-kitchen goodies you'll want to make right away. And the desserts are simply divine!

So let the spirit of the season surround you as you make this holiday one full of handmade memories—a Christmas from the Heart.

The editors

deck the
halls

THIS HOLIDAY SEASON choose traditional Christmas colors and simple supplies to craft festive decorations everywhere in your holiday home. From stockings and table toppers to wreaths and ornaments, let the spirit of the season guide you to make the perfect accessories for this most wonderful time of the year.

RICKRACK GREETING STOCKINGS Share a message on stockings this year with Rickrack Greeting Stockings, *below*. A bright cotton print forms the body of the stocking with cuffs, heels, and toes in coordinating hues. Vintage-shape circle beads trim the cuffs as rickrack spells out the message. Instructions and patterns start on page 25.

QUILTED SUGAR COOKIE TABLE TOPPER Quilt a plate of cookies to display on your holiday table this year. The Quilted Sugar Cookie Table Topper, *opposite*, features your favorite cookie-cutter shapes. Each cookie is embellished with sweet little trims—beads, embroidery stitches, buttons, rickrack, and other special holiday favorites. Instructions and patterns start on page 24.

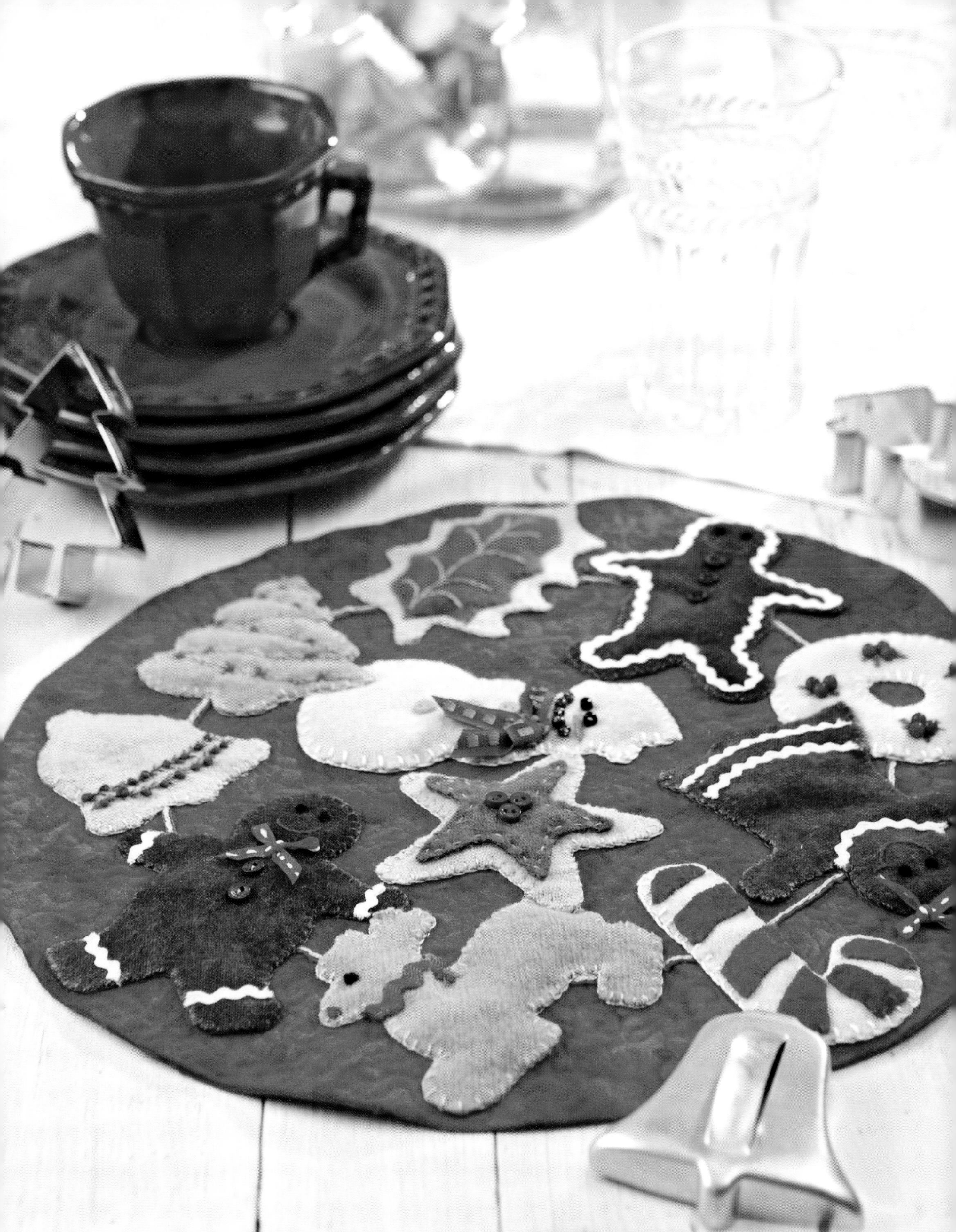

CHRISTMAS RED BIRD TRIM Red glitter outlines the shape of a pretty Christmas Red Bird Trim, *opposite* and *above*. The wings are designed so the bird looks as though it might take flight.

SNOWFLAKE ART BALL A simple white ornament becomes a lovely Snowflake Art Ball, *opposite* and *above right*, when it is trimmed with tiny red snowflakes.

HOLIDAY TREE TRIMS Rub-on transfers make the pretty print design on Holiday Tree Trims, *opposite* and *right*. The shape and size of the tree is determined by the transfer you choose. Little snowflakes and red rhinestones add the sparkle.

PEPPERMINT-SWIRL GIFT PACKAGE They will wonder what special gift you've hidden in the Peppermint-Swirl Gift Package, *opposite* and *below right*. The box is painted and then tied up with clear cellophane. For more trims on the tree shown, *opposite*, turn the page. Instructions and patterns for all the projects start on page 19.

WINTER REINDEER ORNAMENT Cardstock is cut and layered to make a Winter Reindeer Ornament, *above left*. The individual pieces of the reindeer shapes are put together to make the trim 3-dimensional. A tiny festive wreath adorns this little reindeer's neck. Instructions and patterns begin on page 20.

WOODEN STOCKING ORNAMENT Look through scrapbooking or wrapping supplies with a fresh eye and you'll discover a myriad of possibilities for decoupaging wooden cutout ornaments. Make a whimsical Wooden Stocking Ornament, *above right*, by chosing a bright print paper and embellishing it with jingle bells. Instructions are on page 20.

PEPPERMINT ORNAMENT A simple papier mâché disc and paper cupcake cups combine to make a Sweet Candy Trim, *above left*, to hang on your holiday tree. Bright red paint forms the candy swirls and the cupcake cups make the candy ends. Instructions and patterns start on page 18.

SNOW-CONE ORNAMENT Dress up ordinary foam balls quick as a wink with a sprinkling of shimmering cellophane glitter flakes. The lightweight foam ball then rests in a paper cone to make the Snow-Cone Ornament, *top right*, seem almost real. Instructions are on page 19.

STAMPED PAPER ORNAMENT The shape of the stamp that you choose determines the shape of your holiday Stamped Paper Ornament, *above right*. The printed paper and embellishments you choose will show your personal style. Instructions are on page 18.

WELCOMING FELT WREATH Full of warmth and texture, this Welcoming Felt Wreath, *opposite*, features an assortment of wool variations. Double-layered felt leaves are machine stitched before the top fabric is clipped to reveal the layer below. The red felted wool berries add a kick of festive color but can easily be switched to beige for a muted wreath that can be enjoyed all winter long. Instructions and patterns are on page 22.

GOOD CHEER GREETING Extra-large cookies are decorated and hung with pretty star hangers to create a Good Cheer Greeting, *above*, to welcome guests at holiday time. The cookies are draped on an entryway mirror to add some holiday glitz. Instructions begin on page 24.

CANDY CANE TREAT HOLDERS Inexpensive green peat pots hold handfuls of sweet treats enclosed in candy-cane striped tissue paper. The Candy Cane Treat Holders, *opposite* and *below right*, are then tied with green satin bows. Instructions are on page 24.

MAKING MERRY MEMO Scrawl an exuberant "Joy" across a silver-frame mirror, *opposite* and *below*. White sponge-painted snowballs add a frosty finish to the looking glass, which amplifies the shimmer of discount-store glass candle holders and a clear cylinder overflowing with shiny orbs showcased on the sideboard.

Sweet Candy Trim
Shown on page 13

WHAT YOU NEED
Papier-mâché disc
Acrylic crafts paints: red and white
Tracing paper; pencil
Graphite transfer paper
Artist's brushes: ½-inch-wide flat and
    small round
Clear glaze, such as Krylon Crystal
    Clear Glaze
Silver glitter glue
Cupcake cups
Hot-glue gun and glue sticks
¼-inch-wide red-and-white-check
    grosgrain ribbon

WHAT YOU DO
1. Paint the papier mâché disc white; let
dry. Trace the peppermint swirl pattern,
below, onto tracing paper. Using graphite
paper, transfer the peppermint swirl
pattern to the disc. Paint alternating swirl
sections red; let dry. Apply two or three
coats of glaze, letting it dry between coats.

2. Apply silver glitter glue to the edges of
two cupcake cups; let dry. Fold each cup in
half and then accordion-fold to create the
candy-wrapper ends. Hot-glue a wrapper
end to each side of the ornament back. For
a hanger, cut an 8-inch length of ribbon,
make a loop, and knot the ends. Hot-glue
the knotted end of the ribbon to the back
of the ornament.

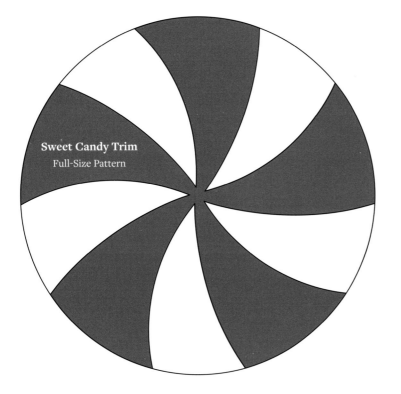

Sweet Candy Trim
Full-Size Pattern

Stamped Paper Ornaments
Shown on page 13

WHAT YOU NEED
Ornament stamp
Cardstock: assorted patterns and red glitter
Snowflake paper punch
Adhesive-back foam dots
Crafts glue
Embellishments: red bows and
    red rhinestones
Fine red cord

WHAT YOU DO
1. Using the ornament stamp as a template,
stamp and then cut out the ornament back
from red glitter cardstock. Stamp and cut
the remaining ornament components using
patterned cardstock as desired. (Stamp the
back side of the paper to conserve your
inventory.) Punch snowflake shapes from
red glitter cardstock.

2. Assemble the ornaments using foam dots
to create a dimensional look. Use crafts glue
to adhere rhinestones, bow embellishments,
and a loop of red cord for hanging.

Christmas Red Bird Trim
Shown on page 11

WHAT YOU NEED
Tracing paper
Pencil
Cardstock: solid red and red glitter
Spray adhesive
Crafts knife
Red glitter glue
Small round artist's brush
Black sequin or bead
Crafts glue
½-inch-wide red satin ribbon
Hot-glue gun and glue sticks

WHAT YOU DO

1. Using spray adhesive, adhere a layer of red glitter card stock over solid red card stock. Let dry. Trace the patterns, *below*. Use the patterns to cut out the bird's body, wing, and tail shapes from the papers. Cut the slits on each cutout shape as indicated on the pattern.

2. Using a small round brush, apply red glitter glue around the edges of each shape. Use crafts glue to adhere a black sequin or bead onto the head for an eye; let dry. Assemble the bird.

3. For a hanger, cut a length of satin ribbon, form a loop, and tie the ends in a knot. Hot-glue the loop in place on the back of the bird's body.

Snow-Cone Ornament
Shown on page 13

WHAT YOU NEED
Papier-mâché cone
Clear glaze, such as Krylon Crystal
   Clear Glaze
Hot-glue gun and glue sticks
Red braided cord
Foam ball
Crafts glue
Iridescent glitter flakes
Wide red satin ribbon

WHAT YOU DO

1. Apply two or three coats of glaze to the cone, letting it dry between coats. Cut a length of red braided cord and hot-glue the ends to opposite sides of the inside edge of the cone opening.

2. Apply a coat of crafts glue to the foam ball and sprinkle with iridescent glitter flakes; let dry. Glue the glittered ball into the cone.

3. Cut a length of wide red satin ribbon and tie in a bow. Hot-glue the bow in place on the front of the cone ornament.

Christmas Red Bird Wings
Full-Size Pattern

Christmas Red Bird Body
Full-Size Pattern

Christmas Red Bird Tail
Full-Size Pattern

Snowflake Art Ball
Shown on page 11

WHAT YOU NEED
Red glitter cardstock
Snowflake paper punches
White ball ornament
Glue stick
½-inch-wide red-and-white-striped
    satin ribbon
Crafts glue

WHAT YOU DO
1. Punch snowflake shapes from red glitter
cardstock. Use the glue stick to adhere the
snowflake shapes to the ornament as
desired; let dry.
2. For a hanger, cut an 8-inch length of
ribbon, thread through the ornament loop,
and knot the ends. Cut another length of
ribbon and tie a bow. Adhere the bow to the
ribbon hanger with crafts glue and let dry.

Winter Reindeer Ornament
Shown on page 12

WHAT YOU NEED
Tracing paper; pencil
Heavyweight punch
Heavy white cardstock
Spray adhesive
Crafts knife
Red braided cord
2 square red brads
Hot-glue gun and glue sticks
Miniature wreath

WHAT YOU DO
1. Using spray adhesive, adhere three
pieces of heavy white cardstock together.
Trace patterns, *opposite*, and cut out
reindeer shapes. Assemble the reindeer
body. Punch a small hole in the assembled
reindeer's hip and shoulder and insert a
square red brad in each hole.
2. For a hanger, cut a length of red braided
cord and knot each end. Hot-glue the hanger
to the backs of the brads. Slide the miniature
wreath over the reindeer's head and onto its
neck. Attach the ear and antler shapes.

Wooden Stocking Ornament
Shown on page 12

WHAT YOU NEED
Purchased wood stocking ornament
Acrylic crafts paints: red and white
½-inch-wide artist's paintbrush
Patterned paper
Crafts glue; jingle bells
Clear glaze, such as Krylon Crystal
    Clear Glaze
Hot-glue gun and glue sticks
1-inch-wide red satin ribbon

WHAT YOU DO
1. Paint the stocking bright red and the
stocking cuff white; let dry.
2. Trace the ornament shape onto
patterned paper and cut it out. Brush a coat
of crafts glue onto the stocking and adhere
the paper cutout in place; let dry. Apply two
or three coats of glaze to the entire stocking
front, letting it dry between coats.
3. Glue jingle bells to stocking shape. Cut
a length of satin ribbon, form a loop, and
hot-glue the loop ends in place on the
stocking cuff. Cut another length of satin
ribbon, tie in a bow, and hot-glue in place.

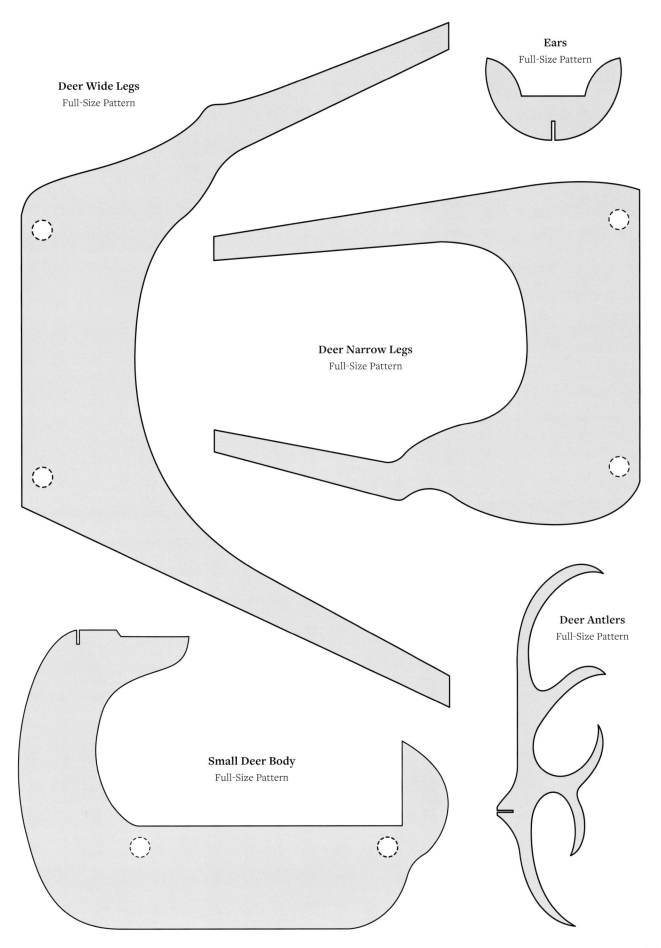

Deer Wide Legs
Full-Size Pattern

Ears
Full-Size Pattern

Deer Narrow Legs
Full-Size Pattern

Small Deer Body
Full-Size Pattern

Deer Antlers
Full-Size Pattern

Holiday Tree Trims
Shown on page 10

WHAT YOU NEED
Holiday rub-on transfers
White paper
Cardstock: white and red glitter
Paper adhesive
Crafts knife
Snowflake paper punch
Adhesive foam dots
Adhesive-back red rhinestone trim

WHAT YOU DO
1. Cut out the desired tree image from a holiday rub-on transfer sheet. Place the image on white paper and rub over the design to transfer. Layer the paper with the transferred image onto white cardstock and secure with paper adhesive; let dry. Use a crafts knife to cut out the tree shape through all paper layers.

2. Punch a snowflake from red glitter cardstock and adhere to the transfer with an adhesive foam dot. Embellish ornament with red rhinestone trim as desired.

Paper Ornaments
Shown on page 11

WHAT YOU NEED
Ornament stamp
Cardstock: assorted patterns
    and red glitter
Snowflake paper punch
Adhesive-back foam dots
Crafts glue
Embellishments: red bows
    and red rhinestones
Fine red cord

WHAT YOU DO
1. Using the ornament stamp as a template, stamp and then cut out the ornament back from red glitter cardstock. Stamp and cut the remaining ornament components using patterned cardstock as desired. (Stamp the back side of the paper to conserve your inventory.) Punch snowflake shapes from red glitter cardstock.

2. Assemble the ornaments using foam dots to create a dimensional look. Use crafts glue to adhere rhinestones, bow embellishments, and a loop of red cord for hanging.

Welcoming Felt Wreath
Shown on page 14

WHAT YOU NEED
Tracing paper
Pencil
35% wool nonwoven felt: wheat fields,
    vanilla latte, white, and red
100% wool nonwoven felt: white, dark
    red, and putty (**Note:** Real wool felt
    products are more substantive and
    hold their shape better than acrylic
    counterparts.)
Chalk fabric marking pencils, such as
    Frixion heat sensitive marking pen
    (**Note:** Thermo-sensitive ink disappears
    with low iron heat.)
Off-white machine quilting thread
Red thread
12-inch wire wreath frame
Mat ruler
Sewing machine
Rotary cutter
Scissors
Straight pins

WHAT YOU DO
1. Trace the patterns, *opposite*. Each leaf pair features a bigger outer leaf in a darker shade and a smaller inner leaf in a lighter shade. Use darkest shades (vanilla latte and wheatfields) for the biggest leaves. Cut enough big leaves to encircle the frame, approximately 18 pairs. Cut the smaller leaf pairs out of putty and the two different felt weights of white. You'll need approximately 12 pairs to place around the inside of the frame.

2. Stack the smaller leaves on top of their larger mates. Note the vein lines marked on the center of the patterns. If you find it helpful, use the marking pen/chalk to lightly mark these stitching lines.

3. With your sewing machine threaded with quilting thread, stitch each pair together by creating the center vein seams. Begin at the base of the leaf stitch toward the leaf point,

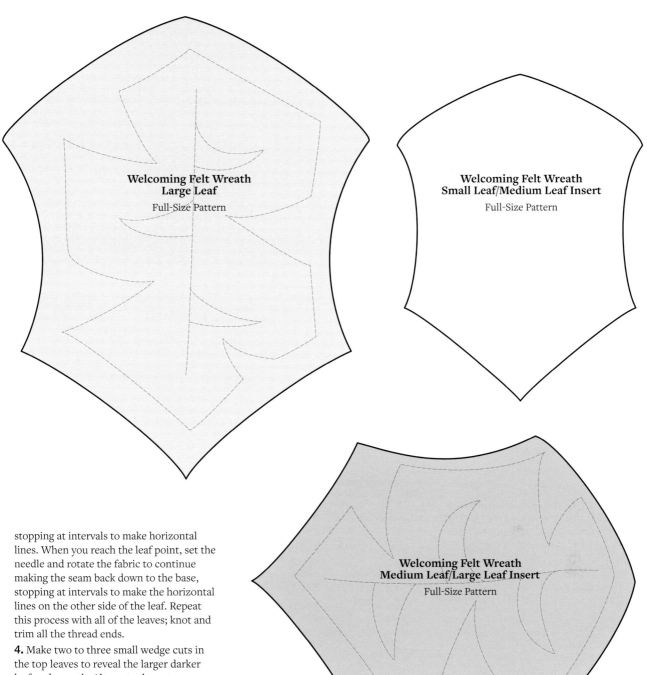

**Welcoming Felt Wreath
Large Leaf**

Full-Size Pattern

**Welcoming Felt Wreath
Small Leaf/Medium Leaf Insert**

Full-Size Pattern

**Welcoming Felt Wreath
Medium Leaf/Large Leaf Insert**

Full-Size Pattern

stopping at intervals to make horizontal lines. When you reach the leaf point, set the needle and rotate the fabric to continue making the seam back down to the base, stopping at intervals to make the horizontal lines on the other side of the leaf. Repeat this process with all of the leaves; knot and trim all the thread ends.

4. Make two to three small wedge cuts in the top leaves to reveal the larger darker leaf underneath. Alternate the cuts on either side of the leaf and use the stitching lines to help guide the shape of your cuts.

5. Arrange the largest leaves around the frame, leaf bases on the inside and leaf point on the outside. Be careful to evenly distribute the colors around the circle. Move the leaves to one side and then begin stitching the underside of the first leaf to the frame. It will take four stitches to connect the leaf to each of the four wires. Tie off the thread and then repeat the process to connect the remaining large leaves.

6. Arrange the smaller leaves around the inner circle, aligning their bases over the bases of the large leaves. Handstitch the undersides of these small leaves to the larger leaves under them. Leave the leaf points untethered.

7. Fold the red felt in half and use the mat ruler and rotary cutter to cut ½-inch strips (approximately 14 inches long). Stack the red strip over the light strip and tightly roll them together. Keep rolling until the piece is ⅞ inch in diameter for the small berry or 1¼ inches in diameter for the larger berry. Use red thread and a sewing needle to stitch the rolled berry together, making stitches back and forth across the center of the bead. Once the center of the bead is stabilized, make a few small stitches to tack down the end of the outer strip.

Alternate stacking the lighter red strip over the darker strip to add variety to the berries. You need six large berries and six small berries to make six two-berry groupings around the wreath.

8. Arrange the berry pairs around the inside of the wreath and stitch them to the inside of the wreath over the base of the smaller felt leaves.

Peppermint-Swirl Gift Package

Shown on page 11

WHAT YOU NEED

Round papier-mâché box
Acrylic crafts paints: red and white
Tracing paper
Graphite transfer paper
Artist's brush: ½-inch-wide flat and
    small round
Clear cellophane wrap
Rubber bands; transparent tape
Glaze medium
½-inch-wide red satin ribbon

WHAT YOU DO

1. Paint the papier-mâché box and lid white; let dry. Trace the peppermint swirl pattern, *page 18*, onto tracing paper. Enlarge as needed to fit box. Using graphite paper, transfer the peppermint swirl pattern to the disk. Paint alternating swirl sections on the box lid and alternating stripes on the box bottom with red paint; let dry. Apply two or three coats of glaze, letting it dry between coats.

2. Lay a double layer of clear cellophane wrap on a flat surface. Center the painted box upside down on top of the cellophane.

Wrap the cellophane toward the box bottom and secure the seam with transparent tape. Gather the cellophane ends and secure with rubber bands. Wrap a length of red satin ribbon around each gathered cellophane end and tie it in a bow.

3. For the tree topper, cut a hole in the box and cellophane for the top tree branch. Insert the topper on the tree.

Good Cheer Greeting

Shown on page 15

WHAT YOU NEED

Large cookies in desired shapes with
    holes made before baking
Royal icing; red sugar sprinkles
Decorative star hooks
Silver bead garland

WHAT YOU DO

1. Decorate cookies as desired using royal icing. Add red sugar sprinkles on the red frosting. Allow to dry until hard. Insert star hook into hole of each cookie. Attach hooks to silver bead garland. Hang on mirror or hooks.

Note: Cookies are for decorating purposes only.

Candy Cane Treat Holders

Shown on page 16

WHAT YOU NEED

Green peat pots
Red-and-white tissue paper
Apple green satin ribbon
Scissors
Treats such as candy or small Christmas
    items

WHAT YOU DO

1. Be sure peat pot is clean. Remove any labels. Cut a piece of tissue paper about 12×12 inches. Tuck the paper into the pot.

2. Fill the tissue cavity with treats. Pull up the tissue around the treats and tie with ribbon. Trim the ribbon ends.

Quilted Sugar Cookie Table Topper

Shown on page 9

WHAT YOU NEED

Tracing paper; pencil
Marking pen
Favorite cookie cutters (optional)
Two 14-inch squares red cotton fabric
28 inches contrasting narrow cording
16×16-inch piece fusible webbing
Scraps: cream, tan, and brown felted wool
    for cookie shapes
Scraps: red, green, and yellow felted wool
    for embellishments
1 yard tiny white rickrack trim
Scraps: ⅛-inch-wide red ribbon for
    embellishments
⅛ yard of ⅜-inch-wide red ribbon for
    snowman scarf
Red rickrack trim
20-22 assorted colors 6.0 mm glass beads
10-12 assorted colors tiny buttons
12 red seed beads
7-14 black seed beads
Coordinating colors embroidery floss or
    perle cotton
Matching sewing thread
14-inch square thin cotton batting
Cotton batting scraps for underneath each
    cookie shape

WHAT YOU DO

1. Enlarge the patterns, *opposite* and *page 26*, and trace patterns onto tracing paper and cut out. Or, trace around favorite cookie cutter shapes onto tracing paper. Cut two large circles for the plate front and back from red cotton fabric. Mark line for inside circle by placing tracing paper underneath pattern and on top of plate front fabric.

Rickrack Greeting Stockings
Shown on page 7

WHAT YOU NEED
Tracing paper; pencil; marking pen
⅓ yard cotton fabric for stocking and
   lining pieces
¼ yard cotton fabric for cuff and
   cuff lining pieces
Two 12×16-inch pieces thin
   cotton batting
Coordinating-color embroidery floss
37 inches medium rickrack for
   around stocking
1 yard baby rickrack for lettering on cuff
Ten ⅝-inch circle-shape pearl beads
Matching sewing threads
Nylon thread or fishing line

WHAT YOU DO

1. Enlarge and trace patterns, *page 27,* onto tracing paper and cut out. Cut two stocking pieces for outside fabric and two for lining. Cut four for cuff pieces and one each of heel and toe pieces. Layer the stocking pieces with batting and lining pieces. Quilt as desired.

2. Press ½ inch under on inside edges of heel and toe pieces. Place heel and toe patches on top of stocking fronts and stitch in place, using two strands embroidery floss to make blanket stitches along folded edges. Baste medium rickrack around side and lower edges of stocking fronts, placing half the trim just inside the ½-inch stitching line. With right sides together, stitch stocking front to back along the side and lower edges, using ½-inch seam line. Clip curves, overcast edges, turn, and press.

3. With marking pen, make lettering on stocking cuff front. Pin baby rickrack in a continuous line over lettering marks. Stitch in place using matching thread. With right sides facing, sew cuff to cuff back along side seams, using ½-inch seam. Join the cuff facings together in the same manner. With right sides together, pin cuff to cuff facing and stitch lower edges together in ½-inch seam. Turn and press. Using nylon thread or fishing line, stitch circular beads to the bottom edge of cuff front.

4. Make hanging loop by cutting a scrap piece of fabric to 2½×8½ inches. Fold fabric in half lengthwise with right sides together and stitch ½-inch seam along long edge. Turn right side out and press. Baste hanging loop on the inside of the stocking at the side edge of stocking.

Place cuff inside stocking with cuff right side facing lining side of stocking. Pin along top edge and stitch in place, using ½-inch seam line. Flip cuff to outside and press lightly along top stitching line.

2. Trace around inside circle line. Sew narrow cording to plate front over line marked for inside circle, forming rim of plate. Trace shapes onto fusible webbing. Cut out centers of paper, leaving only outside edge to fuse to back of felted wool fabric. Cut out wool shapes along fusible webbing lines marked.

3. Cut batting pieces just slightly smaller than cookie shapes. Arrange cookie shapes on plate front, making sure to keep edges of wool shapes at least ½ inch from outside edge of plate fabric to allow for seam allowance. Insert batting underneath shapes and fuse in place.

4. Blanket-stitch around shapes' outside edges using two strands embroidery floss or matching perle cotton.

5. Trace patterns for center shapes for holly, star, bell, and candy cane cookies onto fusible webbing and fuse to the back of wool fabrics. Fuse to the background cookie shapes to form the appearance of frosting. Stitch around pieces by hand or machine using coordinating thread. Embellish each cookie shape with beads, embroidery floss, rickrack, ribbon, and buttons as desired.

6. With right sides together, layer top, backing fabric, and batting. Stitch around outside edges of circle, using a ¼-inch seam line and leaving an opening for turning. Trim batting close to stitching line, clip curves, turn, and press. Slipstitch opening closed. Quilt as desired.

**Quilted
Sugar Cookie Table Topper**
Enlarge 300%
Cut 2

Quilted Sugar Cookie Table Topper
Enlarge 150%

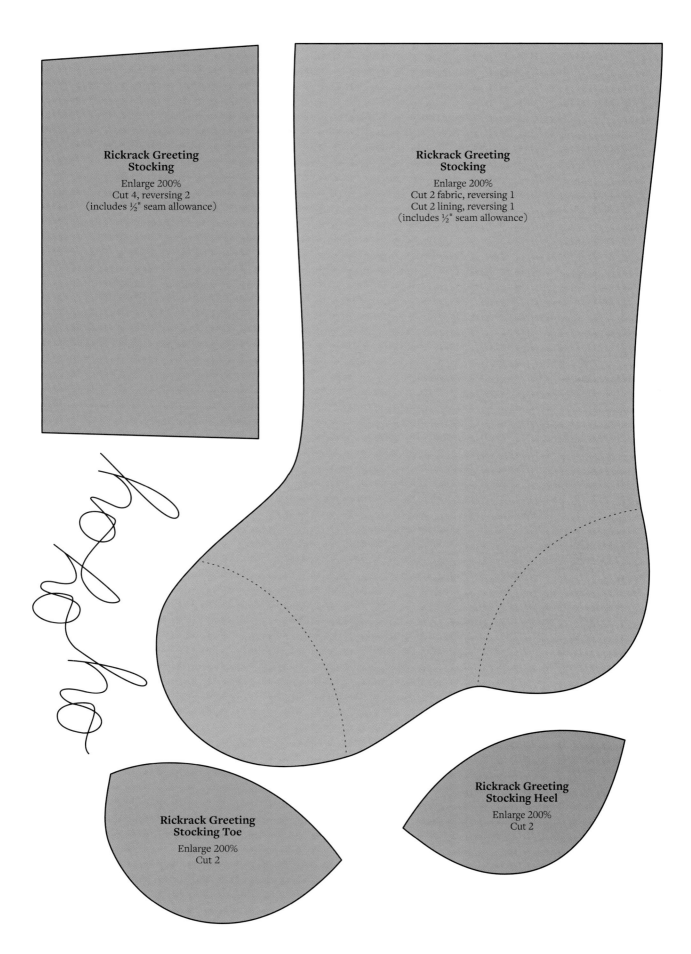

**Rickrack Greeting
Stocking**

Enlarge 200%
Cut 4, reversing 2
(includes ½" seam allowance)

**Rickrack Greeting
Stocking**

Enlarge 200%
Cut 2 fabric, reversing 1
Cut 2 lining, reversing 1
(includes ½" seam allowance)

**Rickrack Greeting
Stocking Toe**

Enlarge 200%
Cut 2

**Rickrack Greeting
Stocking Heel**

Enlarge 200%
Cut 2

stir up some
comfort

NOTHING RADIATES THE CHRISTMAS spirit as warmly as the timeless classics that hold a special place in your loved ones' hearts. Whether it's baking and decorating sugar cookies or gathering the family on Christmas eve for oyster stew, everyone takes comfort in sharing meaningful traditions.

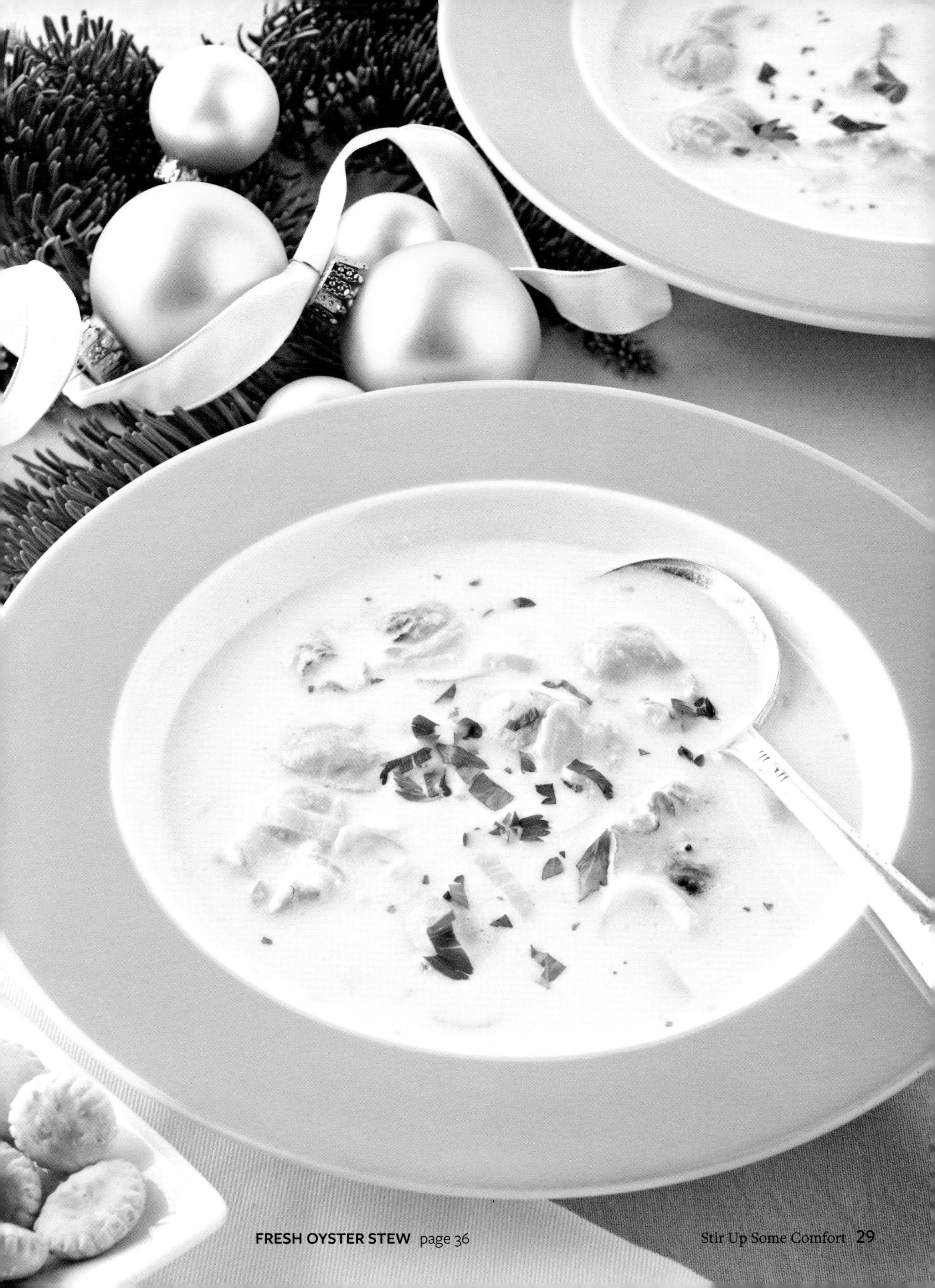

FRESH OYSTER STEW page 36

IT WOULDN'T FEEL LIKE CHRISTMAS without the favorite dishes that families look forward to every year. Supreme Green Bean Casserole, *opposite,* flavored with a wine and mushroom cream sauce, makes a lovely side at any holiday feast. Guests will have a difficult time keeping their hands off tender, warm Herbed Parker House Rolls, *top left.* Sweet Potato Bake, *above right,* is crowned with billowy marshmallows and crunchy pecans, making the dish extra indulgent. Bacon Cheddar Cheese Ball, *above left,* is the perfect appetizer for mingling and munching at casual get-togethers. Recipes begin on page 36.

SCRUMPTIOUS COOKIES AND COCOA make their dazzling appearance at festivities all season long. No cookie tray is complete without Grandmother's Old-Fashioned Sugar Cookie Cutouts, *opposite*, or Red Hot Spritz, *below left*. Lemony Gingerbread Cutouts, *center left*, are another signature sweet as well as Creamy Hot Cocoa, *below*, and Chocolate-Covered Cherry Cookies, *above*. Recipes begin on page 37.

PLEASE YOUR GUESTS with tempting treats—both sweet and savory—as well as something festive to sip. Let them devour Snickerdoodles and Brown Sugar Icebox Cookies, *opposite.* Showcase Cinnamon Swirl Bread, *right,* on a brunch buffet. Entice chocolate lovers with a sweet bite of bliss—Bumpy Road Fudge, *below.* Classic Party Mix, *center right,* and Eggnog, *below right,* are favorites that most everyone will go for. Recipes begin on page 38.

Fresh Oyster Stew

Settling down to a warm, creamy bowl of oyster stew on Christmas Eve is a genuine pleasure. In this easy recipe, mellow leeks complement the delicate flavor of the oysters. For a richer stew, substitute half-and-half or light cream for the milk.
Shown on page 29

WHAT YOU NEED

4　cups shucked oysters (2 pints)
⅔　cup sliced leeks (2 medium)
2　tablespoons butter
2　tablespoons all-purpose flour
½　teaspoon salt
¼　teaspoon dried tarragon, crushed
2½　cups whole milk
　　Snipped fresh parsley (optional)

WHAT YOU DO

1. Drain oysters, reserving liquid. Strain liquid. Add enough water to strained liquid to measure 2 cups. Set aside. Rinse the oysters thoroughly to remove any sand or shell.
2. In a large saucepan cook leeks in hot butter over medium heat about 4 minutes or until tender, stirring occasionally. Add flour, salt, and tarragon. Slowly add milk. Cook and stir until slightly thickened and bubbly. Cook and stir for 1 minute more. Keep warm.
3. In a medium saucepan combine reserved oyster liquid and oysters. Bring just to simmering over medium heat; reduce heat. Cook, covered, for 1 to 2 minutes or until oysters curl around the edges. Skim and discard fat from surface of cooking liquid.
4. Stir oyster mixture into milk mixture; heat through. If desired, garnish with snipped parsley. Serve immediately. Makes 6 (1-cup) servings.

Bacon Cheddar Cheese Ball

Serve this savory hors d'oeuvre with crackers, toasted baguette slices, celery sticks, or cucumber slices. When mixing everything together, you'll find that it works better if you shred your own cheese rather than buying the preshredded kind.
Shown on page 31

WHAT YOU NEED

8　ounces extra-sharp cheddar cheese, finely shredded (2 cups)
1　8-ounce package reduced-fat cream cheese (Neufchâtel)
½　2-ounce jar sliced pimientos, rinsed, drained, patted dry, and chopped
2　tablespoons apricot preserves
1　tablespoon milk
1½　teaspoons Worcestershire sauce
⅛　teaspoon bottled hot pepper sauce
15　slices bacon, crisp-cooked and drained
¼　cup pistachio nuts, chopped

WHAT YOU DO

1. In a large mixing bowl combine cheddar and cream cheeses; let stand at room temperature for 30 minutes. Add pimientos, apricot preserves, milk, Worcestershire sauce, and hot pepper sauce. Crumble 10 of the bacon slices and add to mixture. Beat with an electric mixer on medium until almost smooth.
2. Crumble remaining bacon. Cover and chill cheese mixture and the remaining bacon about 2 hours or until easy to handle. Shape cheese mixture into a ball. Cover and chill cheese ball for several hours or up to 3 days.
3. Just before serving, roll in crumbled bacon and chopped pistachio nuts. Place cheese ball on a decorative plate. Makes 4 (¼-cup) servings.

Bumpy Road Fudge

For those who like their fudge fully loaded, this decadent treat delivers with marshmallows and pecans.
Shown on page 35

WHAT YOU NEED

4　cups sugar
1¼　cups whipping cream
⅓　cup unsweetened cocoa powder
⅓　cup light-color corn syrup
¼　teaspoon salt
1　tablespoon vanilla
1　cup snipped tiny marshmallows
1　cup chopped pecans, toasted

WHAT YOU DO

1. Line an 8×8×2-inch baking pan with foil, extending the foil over edges of pan. Butter foil; set pan aside.
2. Butter the sides of a 3-quart heavy saucepan. In the saucepan combine sugar, cream, cocoa powder, corn syrup, and salt. Cook and stir over medium heat until mixture is boiling. Clip a candy thermometer to the side of the pan. Reduce heat to medium-low; continue boiling at a moderate, steady rate, stirring occasionally, until thermometer registers 236°F, soft-ball stage (about 10 minutes). (Adjust heat as necessary to maintain a steady boil.)
3. Remove saucepan from heat. Add vanilla but do not stir. Cool, without stirring, to 110°F (1 to 1¼ hours). Remove thermometer from saucepan. Beat mixture vigorously with a clean wooden spoon just until candy starts to thicken. Add marshmallows and pecans. Continue beating just until fudge starts to lose its gloss (6 to 8 minutes total).
4. Immediately spread fudge evenly in prepared pan. Score fudge into squares while warm. Let fudge cool to room temperature. When fudge is firm, use foil edges to lift fudge from pan. Cut into squares. Makes 64 pieces.

To Store: Layer fudge between sheets of waxed paper in an airtight container; cover. Store in the refrigerator for up to 1 week.

Grandmother's Old-Fashioned Sugar Cookie Cutouts

If you only make one cookie at Christmastime, it should be these delicately iced sugar cookies.
Shown on page 33

WHAT YOU NEED

⅔ cup butter, softened
¾ cup granulated sugar
1 teaspoon baking powder
¼ teaspoon salt
1 egg
1 tablespoon milk
1 teaspoon vanilla
2 cups all-purpose flour
  Powdered Sugar Icing
  Colored sugar
  Decorating candies

WHAT YOU DO

1. In a large mixing bowl beat butter on medium to high for 30 seconds. Add granulated sugar, baking powder, and salt. Beat until combined, scraping sides of bowl occasionally. Beat in egg, milk, and vanilla until combined. Beat in as much of the flour as you can with the mixer. Stir in any remaining flour. Divide dough in half. Cover and chill dough about 30 minutes or until easy to handle.
2. Preheat oven to 375°F. On a floured surface, roll half the dough at a time to ⅛- to ¼-inch thickness. Using a 2½-inch cookie cutter, cut into desired shapes. Place 1 inch apart on ungreased cookie sheets.
3. Bake for 7 to 10 minutes or until edges are firm and bottoms are very light brown. Transfer to wire racks and let cool. Frost and decorate as desired with Powdered Sugar Icing, colored sugar, and decorating candies. Makes 36 cookies.

Powdered Sugar Icing: Combine 1 cup powdered sugar, ¼ teaspoon vanilla, and 1 tablespoon milk. If necessary, stir in additional milk, 1 teaspoon at a time, until desired consistency for spreading or piping. Add food coloring as desired.

Red Hot Spritz

These sweet and buttery gems are decked out in red and green to look like miniature wreaths.
Shown on page 32

WHAT YOU NEED

1½ cups butter, softened
1 cup granulated sugar
1 teaspoon baking powder
1 egg
1 teaspoon vanilla
¼ teaspoon almond extract (optional)
3½ cups all-purpose flour
  Powdered Sugar Icing (recipe, below left)
  Colored sugar
  Red cinnamon candies

WHAT YOU DO

1. Preheat oven to 375°F. In a large mixing bowl beat butter with an electric mixer on medium to high for 30 seconds. Add granulated sugar and baking powder. Beat until combined, scraping sides of bowl occasionally. Beat in egg, vanilla, and, if desired, almond extract until combined. Beat in as much of the flour as you can with the mixer. Stir in any remaining flour.
2. Force unchilled dough through a cookie press onto ungreased cookie sheet.
3. Bake for 8 to 10 minutes or until edges are firm but not brown. Transfer to a wire rack and let cool. Frost cookies with Powdered Sugar Icing and decorate with colored sugar and cinnamon candies. Makes 84 cookies.

Chocolate-Covered Cherry Cookies

Shown on page 32

WHAT YOU NEED

1 10-ounce jar (about 42) maraschino cherries, undrained
½ cup butter, softened
1 cup sugar
¼ teaspoon baking powder
¼ teaspoon baking soda
¼ teaspoon salt
1 egg
1½ teaspoons vanilla
½ cup unsweetened cocoa powder
1½ cups all-purpose flour
1 6-ounce package (1 cup) semisweet chocolate pieces
½ cup sweetened condensed milk

WHAT YOU DO

1. Preheat oven to 350°F. Drain cherries; reserve juice. Halve any large cherries; set aside.
2. In a medium mixing bowl beat butter on medium to high for 30 seconds. Add sugar, baking powder, baking soda, and salt. Beat until combined, scraping sides of bowl occasionally. Beat in egg and vanilla. Beat in cocoa powder. Beat in as much of the flour as you can. Stir in any remaining flour.
3. Shape dough into 1-inch balls. Place 2 inches apart on an ungreased cookie sheet. Press your thumb into the center of each ball. Place a cherry in each center.
4. In a saucepan combine chocolate pieces and sweetened condensed milk. Cook and stir over low heat until chocolate is melted. Add 4 teaspoons reserved cherry juice. (For thinner frosting, add additional cherry juice.) Spoon 1 teaspoon of the frosting over each cherry, spreading to cover.
5. Bake about 10 minutes or until edges are firm. Let cool on cookie sheet for 1 minute. Transfer cookies to a wire rack; cool completely. Makes 42 cookies.

Snickerdoodles
Shown on page 34

WHAT YOU NEED
½ cup butter
1 cup sugar
¼ teaspoon baking soda
¼ teaspoon cream of tartar
1 egg
½ teaspoon vanilla
1½ cups all-purpose flour
2 tablespoons sugar
1 teaspoon ground cinnamon

WHAT YOU DO
1. In a medium mixing bowl beat the butter with an electric mixer for 30 seconds. Add the 1 cup sugar, baking soda, and cream of tartar. Beat until combined, scraping sides of bowl. Beat in the egg and vanilla until combined. Beat in as much of the flour as you can with the mixer. Stir in remaining flour with a wooden spoon. Cover and chill for 1 hour.
2. Preheat oven to 375°F. In a small mixing bowl combine the 2 tablespoons sugar and the cinnamon. Shape dough into 1-inch balls. Roll balls in sugar-cinnamon mixture to coat. Place balls 2 inches apart on an ungreased cookie sheet. Bake for 10 to 11 minutes or until edges are golden. Transfer cookies to wire racks; cool. Makes 36 cookies.

To Store: Place cookies in layers separated by waxed paper in an airtight container. Store at room temperature for up to 3 days or freeze for up to 3 months.

Brown Sugar Icebox Cookies
Shown on page 34

WHAT YOU NEED
½ cup shortening
½ cup butter, softened
1¼ cups packed brown sugar
½ teaspoon baking soda
¼ teaspoon salt
1 egg
1 teaspoon vanilla
2½ cups all-purpose flour
¾ cup toasted ground hazelnuts (filberts) or pecans
⅔ cup finely chopped toasted hazelnuts (filberts) or pecans (optional)
Milk chocolate, melted (optional)

WHAT YOU DO
1. In a large mixing bowl beat shortening and butter with an electric mixer on medium to high for 30 seconds. Add the brown sugar, baking soda, and salt. Beat until combined, scraping sides of bowl occasionally. Beat in egg and vanilla until combined. Beat in as much of the flour as you can with the mixer. Stir in remaining flour and the ¾ cup ground nuts with a wooden spoon.
2. Divide dough in half. On waxed paper, shape each half into a 10-inch-long roll. Lift and smooth the waxed paper to help shape the rolls. If desired, roll the cookie rolls in the ⅔ cup chopped nuts. Wrap each roll in plastic wrap. Chill in the refrigerator for at least 4 hours or until firm enough to slice. (Or wrap dough in foil and freeze for up to 3 months; thaw in the refrigerator before slicing.)
3. Preheat oven to 375°F. Cut rolls into ¼-inch-thick slices. Place slices 1 inch apart on an ungreased cookie sheet. Bake for 10 minutes or until edges are firm. Transfer cookies to wire racks; cool. If desired, drizzle melted chocolate over cookies. Makes 60 cookies.

To Store: Place cookies in layers separated by waxed paper in an airtight container; cover. Store drizzled cookies at room temperature for up to 3 days. Freeze undrizzled cookies for up to 3 months. Thaw and drizzle with melted chocolate.

Lemony Gingerbread Cutouts
Shown on page 32

WHAT YOU NEED
2 cups all-purpose flour
½ cup whole wheat flour
¾ teaspoon baking soda
½ teaspoon ground cinnamon
½ teaspoon ground cloves
½ cup butter, softened
½ cup sugar
⅓ cup molasses
1 egg
1 tablespoon grated fresh ginger
2 teaspoons finely shredded lemon peel
Powdered Sugar Icing (recipe, page 37)
Colored sugar (optional)

WHAT YOU DO
1. In a medium bowl combine all-purpose flour, whole wheat flour, baking soda, cinnamon, and cloves; set aside.
2. In a large mixing bowl beat butter on medium to high for 30 seconds. Add sugar; beat until combined. Add molasses and egg; beat until combined. Beat in as much of the flour mixture as you can. Stir in any remaining flour mixture, the ginger, and lemon peel. Divide dough in half. Cover and chill dough about 3 hours or until easy to handle.
3. Preheat oven to 350°F. Grease a cookie sheet; set aside. On a lightly floured surface, roll one portion of dough to ¼ inch thick. Using 2-inch cookie cutters, cut out dough. Place cutouts 1 inch apart on prepared cookie sheet. Repeat with remaining dough.
4. Bake for 8 to 10 minutes or until edges are firm. Cool cookies on cookie sheet for 1 minute. Transfer cookies to a wire rack and let cool.
5. Decorate cookies with Powdered Sugar Icing and, if desired, colored sugar. Makes 24 cookies.

Sweet Potato Bake

In this classic comfort dish, sticky marshmallows and toasted pecans top creamy pureed sweet potatoes. This recipe feeds a crowd. And the baking dish will look perfect on the table.
Shown on page 31

WHAT YOU NEED

4½ pounds sweet potatoes
2 tablespoons olive oil
1 tablespoon kosher salt
½ cup butter
⅔ cup whipping cream
2 tablespoons pure maple syrup
¼ teaspoon ground nutmeg
1 teaspoon kosher salt
2 to 3 cups tiny marshmallows
¼ cup coarsely chopped pecan halves, toasted

WHAT YOU DO

1. Preheat oven to 350°F. Scrub potatoes and prick with a fork. Brush with olive oil. Sprinkle with 1 tablespoon salt. Place potatoes in a 15×10×1-inch baking pan. Roast, uncovered, for 30 to 40 minutes or until soft. Cool until easy to handle.
2. Increase oven temperature to 450°F. Halve potatoes; scoop out flesh and discard skin. Press through a fine-mesh sieve. Transfer to a large bowl.
3. In a small saucepan combine butter and cream; cook over medium heat until mixture comes to a simmer. Fold into the sweet potatoes along with the maple syrup, nutmeg, and 1 teaspoon salt. Transfer to a 2-quart baking dish.
4. Sprinkle marshmallows on potatoes. Bake, uncovered, for 12 to 15 minutes or until marshmallows are golden brown. Sprinkle with toasted pecans. Serve immediately. Makes 8 servings.

To Make Ahead: Up to 1 day ahead, prepare through Step 3. Cover and refrigerate. To reheat, bake, covered, in a 350°F oven for 55 minutes, stirring once. Increase oven temperature to 450°F. Uncover and proceed with Step 4.

Supreme Green Bean Casserole

Here is a sophisticated take on the traditional canned soup casserole of years past. Short and thin French-style green beans are baked in a homemade creamy wine sauce and topped with crispy fried shallots.
Shown on page 30

WHAT YOU NEED

1½ pounds haricots verts or thin green beans, trimmed
4 slices bacon
1½ pounds assorted sliced mushrooms, such as stemmed shiitake, cremini, and button
6 garlic, minced
1 tablespoon snipped fresh thyme
½ teaspoon salt
½ teaspoon ground black pepper
2 tablespoons butter
2 tablespoons all-purpose flour
1½ cups half-and-half or light cream
½ cup dry white wine
½ cup finely shredded Parmesan cheese (2 ounces)
⅛ teaspoon salt
⅛ teaspoon ground black pepper
⅓ cup pine nuts, toasted (optional)
½ cup vegetable oil
4 shallots, thinly sliced crosswise, or 1 cup thinly sliced sweet onion

WHAT YOU DO

1. Preheat oven to 375°F. Grease a 2-quart casserole; set aside. In a 12-inch skillet cook beans in enough lightly salted boiling water to cover for 3 to 5 minutes or until crisp-tender; drain. Transfer beans to a bowl of ice water to stop cooking. Drain again. Wipe skillet dry.
2. In the same skillet cook bacon over medium heat until crisp. Remove from skillet, reserving drippings; drain on paper towels. When cool, finely crumble or chop bacon; set aside.

3. Meanwhile, add mushrooms, garlic, and thyme to the bacon drippings in the skillet; cook and stir for 5 to 6 minutes or until mushrooms are tender and excess liquid has evaporated. Stir in crumbled bacon, the ½ teaspoon salt, and ½ teaspoon pepper. Gently toss mushroom mixture with beans.
4. For sauce, in a small saucepan melt butter over medium heat. Stir in flour. Stir in half-and-half and wine. Cook and stir over medium heat until thickened and bubbly. Stir in the Parmesan cheese, the ⅛ teaspoon salt, and the ⅛ teaspoon pepper. Pour sauce over green bean mixture, stirring gently just until combined. Transfer green bean mixture to prepared casserole.
5. Bake about 25 minutes or until bubbly and beans are tender. Let stand for 10 minutes. Stir green bean mixture. If desired, sprinkle bean mixture with pine nuts.
6. Meanwhile, in a small saucepan heat oil over medium-high heat. Add sliced shallots in small batches and cook about 1½ minutes or until golden and slightly crisp. Using a slotted spoon, transfer shallots to paper towels to drain. Top casserole with fried shallots just before serving. Makes 8 servings.

To Make Ahead: Prepare as directed through Step 4. Cover casserole. Cook shallots as directed in Step 6. Drain and transfer to an airtight storage container. Chill casserole and shallots for up to 24 hours. To serve, let casserole stand at room temperature for 30 minutes before baking as directed in Step 5. Reheat shallots in microwave. Top baked casserole with fried shallots and, if desired, pine nuts.

Potluck Perfect

These sweet potato and green bean casseroles are ideal for toting to holiday gatherings. Keep your casserole piping hot as it travels. Cover the dish with foil. Then wrap the dish in kitchen towels and transport it in an insulated carrier.

Herbed Parker House Rolls

These light, puffy yeast rolls, which resemble miniature clutch-style purses, were named for the Parker House Hotel in Boston, where they originated during the late 19th century.
Shown on page 31

WHAT YOU NEED

3   to 3½ cups all-purpose flour
1   package active dry yeast
¼   cup snipped fresh chives or finely chopped green onions (2)
1   tablespoon snipped fresh rosemary
2   cloves garlic, minced (optional)
¾   cup water
¼   cup butter
1   teaspoon sugar
1   teaspoon salt
1   egg
¼   cup mashed potatoes
3   tablespoons butter, melted

WHAT YOU DO

1. In a large bowl combine 1 cup of the flour, the yeast, chives, rosemary, and, if desired, garlic. In a small saucepan heat and stir the water, ¼ cup butter, sugar, and salt until warm (120°F to 130°F) and butter almost melts. Add butter mixture to flour mixture. Add egg and mashed potatoes. Beat with an electric mixer on low to medium for 30 seconds, scraping sides of bowl constantly. Beat on high for 3 minutes. Using a wooden spoon, stir in as much of the remaining flour as you can.
2. Turn out dough onto a lightly floured surface. Knead in enough of the remaining flour to make a moderately stiff dough that is smooth and elastic (6 to 8 minutes total). Shape dough into a ball. Place in a lightly greased bowl, turning once to grease surface. Cover; let rise in a warm place until double in size (about 1 hour).
3. Punch down dough. Turn out onto a lightly floured surface. Cover and let rest for 10 minutes. Grease two large baking sheets; set aside. Roll dough to ¼-inch thickness. Using a floured 2½-inch biscuit cutter, cut into rounds. Brush with some of the 3 tablespoons melted butter. Reroll scraps as necessary.
4. To shape rolls, fold dough rounds in half, making each crease slightly off center. Place rolls, larger halves on top, 2 inches apart on prepared baking sheets. Cover and let rise until nearly double in size (about 30 minutes).
5. Preheat oven to 375°F. Lightly brush tops of rolls with the remaining melted butter. Bake for 12 to 15 minutes or until golden. Serve warm. Makes 35 rolls.

To Make Ahead: Prepare and bake rolls as directed. Place in an airtight freezer container and freeze for up to 1 month. Thaw at room temperature for several hours. To serve, preheat oven to 350°F. Wrap rolls in a layer in foil. Bake for 10 to 12 minutes or until warm.

Cinnamon-Swirl Bread

Bake this comforting classic for breakfast or a brunch—or whenever you are in need of some TLC. Its sweet, warming aroma alone is enough to quickly lift the spirits.
Shown on page 35

WHAT YOU NEED

1⅓ cups sugar
½   cup finely chopped pecans or walnuts, toasted
2   teaspoons ground cinnamon
2   cups all-purpose flour
1   teaspoon baking powder
½   teaspoon salt
1   egg
1   cup milk
⅓   cup vegetable oil

WHAT YOU DO

1. Preheat oven to 350°F. Grease and flour the bottom and ½ inch up the sides of a 9×5×3-inch loaf pan.
2. In a small bowl combine ⅓ cup of the sugar, the nuts, and cinnamon; set aside. In a large bowl combine the remaining 1 cup sugar, the flour, baking powder, and salt. In a medium bowl beat egg with a fork; stir in milk and oil. Add egg mixture all at once to flour mixture. Stir just until moistened (batter should be lumpy).
3. Pour half of the batter into prepared pan. Sprinkle with half of the cinnamon mixture. Repeat with remaining batter and cinnamon mixture. Draw a wide rubber scraper down through batter and up in a circular motion to marble. Bake for 45 to 50 minutes or until a wooden toothpick inserted near the center comes out clean.
4. Cool in pan on a wire rack for 10 minutes. Remove bread from pan. Cool completely on wire rack. Wrap and store bread overnight before slicing. Makes 1 loaf (14 servings).

Classic Party Mix

What began in the 1950s as a recipe promotion to sell more Chex cereal has become an American holiday tradition. While you may still enjoy the classic recipe, you may also want to try some exciting new variations.
Shown on page 35

WHAT YOU NEED

4   cups pretzel sticks
4   cups round toasted oat cereal
4   cups bite-size wheat or bran square cereal
4   cups bite-size rice or corn square cereal
3   cups mixed nuts
1   cup butter or margarine
3   tablespoons Worcestershire sauce
½   teaspoon seasoned salt

WHAT YOU DO

1. Preheat oven to 300°F. In a very large roasting pan combine pretzels, oat cereal, wheat or bran cereal, rice or corn cereal, and nuts. Set aside.
2. In small saucepan combine butter, Worcestershire sauce, and seasoned salt. Heat and stir until butter melts. Drizzle butter mixture over cereal mixture; stir gently to coat.

3. Bake about 45 minutes or until golden, stirring every 15 minutes. Spread on a large piece of foil to cool. Store in an airtight container for up to 1 week. Makes 16 servings.

Tex-Mex Party Mix: Prepare as directed, except substitute shoestring potato sticks for the pretzels, taco sauce for the Worcestershire sauce, and 1 tablespoon chili powder for the salt.

Cajun Party Mix: Prepare as directed, except substitute pecans for the nuts and 1 teaspoon Cajun seasoning for the salt. Add 1 tablespoon bottled hot pepper sauce to the butter mixture.

Curry Party Mix: Prepare as directed, except substitute peanuts for the nuts and 1 tablespoon curry powder for the salt. After baking, stir in 1 cup golden raisins.

Pizza Party Mix: Prepare as directed, except substitute broken melba toast rounds for the pretzels and 1 tablespoon Italian seasoning for the salt. After 30 minutes of baking, stir in ½ cup grated Parmesan cheese.

Sugar-and-Spice Party Mix: Prepare as directed, except substitute ½ cup honey for the Worcestershire sauce and 1 tablespoon apple pie spice for the salt. After baking, stir in 2 cups dried apple chips.

Zoo Party Mix: Prepare as directed, except substitute mini knot pretzels for the pretzel sticks. Substitute bite-size fish-shape crackers and animal crackers for some of the cereal.

A Winter Warmer

Some of the best December days may be ones spent outdoors— going sledding, building a snowman, or taking a peaceful walk through the woods after the first snowfall. Make it warm and inviting by bringing hot cocoa along to share. Prepare the Creamy Hot Cocoa (recipe at right) and tote the beverage in a 1-quart insulated bottle. Be sure to preheat the bottle before adding the cocoa; simply fill the bottle with hot water and let it stand for 10 minutes. Drain the water and add the hot cocoa.

Eggnog

Serve this seasonal specialty without food safety concerns. You cook the eggs before blending the drink together.
Shown on page 35

WHAT YOU NEED

4   egg yolks, beaten
2   cups milk
⅓   cup sugar
1   cup whipping cream
1   to 2 tablespoons light rum
1   to 2 tablespoons bourbon
1   teaspoon vanilla
    Ground nutmeg

WHAT YOU DO

1. In a large heavy saucepan stir together the egg yolks, milk, and sugar. Cook and stir over medium heat until milk mixture just coats a metal spoon; do not let boil.
2. Place the pan in a sink or bowl of ice water and stir for 2 minutes. Stir in whipping cream, rum, bourbon, and vanilla.
3. Cover and chill for 4 to 24 hours. Serve in glasses. Sprinkle with nutmeg. Makes 7 servings.

Lower-Fat Eggnog: Prepare as directed, except omit whipping cream and use 3 cups milk.

Alcohol-Free Eggnog: Prepare as directed, except omit the rum and bourbon and increase the milk to 2⅓ cups.

Creamy Hot Cocoa

You'll capture smiles from young and old alike when you present cups of cocoa crowned with fluffy white marshmallows and embellished with shaved chocolate. Try some other flavors too.
Shown on page 32

WHAT YOU NEED

⅓   cup sugar
⅓   cup unsweetened cocoa powder
4   cups half-and-half, light cream, or whole milk
1   teaspoon vanilla
    Tiny marshmallows (optional)
    Grated chocolate (optional)

WHAT YOU DO

1. In a medium saucepan combine sugar and cocoa powder. Gradually whisk in 1 cup of the half-and-half. Cook and stir over medium-low heat just until mixture comes to boiling. Stir in vanilla.
2. Serve cocoa in cups. If desired, top with marshmallows and grated chocolate. Makes 4 servings.

Minty Hot Cocoa: Prepare as directed, except add 1 tablespoon peppermint schnapps or 2 to 3 drops peppermint extract to each serving. Garnish each serving with a peppermint stick.

Mocha Hot Cocoa: Prepare as directed, except add 1 tablespoon instant espresso powder or instant coffee crystals to the sugar mixture.

Irish Hot Cocoa: Prepare as directed, except add 1 tablespoon Irish cream liqueur to each serving.

Spiced Mexican Hot Cocoa: Prepare as directed, except add ½ to 1 teaspoon ground cinnamon to the sugar mixture. Add ½ teaspoon almond extract with the vanilla. If desired, sprinkle each serving with additional ground cinnamon.

naturally inspired

LET NATURE INSPIRE YOU to create lovely crafts and decorations that quietly whisper Merry Christmas all around. Tiny needle-felted deer tuck into a wreath, the aroma of fresh fruit fills the air, paper birds rest in the trees, and fresh greenery encircles tabletops as nature celebrates Christmas.

WOODLANDS DEER WREATH Needle-felted deer rest in a fresh green wreath to create a Woodlands Deer Wreath, *below*. Three chenille stems are twisted together to form an armature for the deer's body. A foundation layer of plain roving pads the chenille stems before the deer is wrapped in soft beige wool. The wreath is accented with a brown paper bow and red berries. Instructions begin on page 50.

HOLIDAY CITRUS GARLAND Fresh orange slices, textural pinecones, and bright red cranberries combine with sparkling beads to make a naturally beautiful Holiday Citrus Garland, *opposite*. The garland rests nicely on a mantel or can be strung across a holiday table. Instructions begin on page 53.

FELT PINECONES Bits of felt are layered onto wire to create Felt Pinecones, *above*. The trick to giving them dimension is hand-stitching the petals and gathering the centers. Created in lovely shades of golden browns, the pinecones make a perfect focal point on a fabric wreath, on a tree branch, as an ornament, or simply gracing a mantel or coffee table. Instructions and patterns begin on page 50.

CHRISTMAS MESSAGE TREE TRIMS A diminutive tabletop Christmas tree in a rustic copper pot spells out a special holiday message of joy with Joy Ornaments, *opposite*, fashioned from jar lids and linen. Bookworm Birds, *below right*, made from the pages of paperback books flit from branch to branch amid Floral Rosettes, *below left*, made of paper strips and self-adhesive type. Instructions begin on page 52.

STICKS AND STONES WREATH

Combine unexpected shapes from nature to create a Sticks and Stones Wreath, *opposite*, to grace your holiday door this year. A fresh green wreath is adorned with sticks of varied thicknesses and stones wrapped in wire. Instructions are on page 52.

PAPER CONE PINES

Conical shapes grow into statuesque Paper Cone Pines, *above right*, simply by rolling handmade papers to a point and trimming the bottom so each stands straight. For a pretty composition, vary the patterns and heights, then glue a gold bead to the top of each tree. Instructions are on page 53.

CRYSTAL TOPIARY

For a fresh centerpiece, build a Crystal Topiary, *right*, with crystal candlesticks and plates. Use a mix of antique and new finds or purchase matching crystal pieces. Instructions are on page 53.

Woodlands Deer Wreath

Shown on page 43

DIMENSIONS
Doe 3½"H×4½"W, Buck 4"H×4½"W

WHAT YOU NEED
3 beige chenille stems
100% wool roving: beige, white, and a
    pinch of black
Needle-felting needles
3-prong needle felting tool, such as Clover
Felting mat or rigid foam insulation
Scissors
Pinking shears
Brown kraft paper
Fresh green wreath
Twine
Red berries

WHAT YOU DO
To make the deer:
1. Fold the first chenille stem in half; the bend will become the end the deer's snout. Fold both stems down 1 inch from the snout to turn the top of the head and start the neck. Bend 1½ inches of both chenille ends up to make double thick front legs. See Photo A.
2. Fold the second chenille stem in half. Wrap the chenille stem on either side of the fold around the tops of the front legs (by the first chenille stem ends). Let the stems extend straight to form the underbelly. Bend them both down at the 2-inch mark to make the back legs. Bend up the 1½ inches of the chenille stem ends to make double thick legs as you did with the front legs. See Photo B.
3. Fold the third stem in half; the fold will become the deer's tail. Hook the ends of the back legs around the third chenille stem ½ inch from the tail fold. Extend both chenille stems 2½ inches up the deer's back. Wrap the stems around the head once, and then form the leftover 1-inch

ends into antlers. For the female deer, fold the stem ends in half and use them as the base of the ears. See Photo C.
4. Tightly wrap the entire chenille stem armature with small strands of white roving. Place the deer on your felting mat (or rigid foam) and needle-felt the white roving in place.
5. Overwrap the entire deer with beige roving. Needle-felt each new strand in place before adding a new piece.
6. Place more white roving over the deer's chest and under its tail; needle-felt it in place.
7. Roll a strand of beige roving into a ¼-inch to ½-inch-long deer ear. Place it on your felting mat and needle-felt the fibers to hold the shape. Roll a small strand of white roving and needle-felt it to one side of the ear. Hold the ear in position with one hand and poke it into the deer with your other hand. Repeat the process to make and attach the second ear.
8. Use tiny strands of beige and white roving to wrap the chenille antlers. Needle-felt the fibers in place so they don't unravel.
9. Roll the tiniest strands of black roving into two ball-shaped eyes. Needle-felt them directly into the deer's head. Roll a slightly larger strand for the deer's nose; needle-felt it to the end of his snout. See Photo D. Set the deer aside.

To make the wreath:
Wrap the fresh wreath with twine, tucking the ends into the greens. Use pinking shears to cut strips of brown kraft paper into 10×2-inch strips. Loop the paper strips together to form a bow, wiring to secure. Attach to the wreath. Make smaller bows to place randomly on the wreath. Tuck berries into the small bows. Place the deer near the large bow and wire in place.

Felt Pinecones
Shown on page 45

DIMENSIONS
5-petal flower pinecone total length is
    4 inches, actual pinecone 3½ inches
10-petal pinecone total length 2½ inches,
    actual pinecone 3 inches
Felt pine needle ribbon gives the piece
    4 inches of additional length

WHAT YOU NEED
Tracing paper; pencil
35% wool felt, such as National
    Nonwovens: dark green, felt brown,
    mustard, ochre
100% wool: light green, fawn, beige
Off-white sewing thread
Fabric-covered 22-gauge brown floral
    stems
Sewing needle; wire cutters; scissors

A
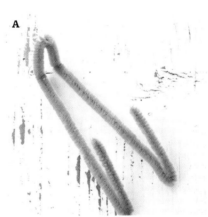

B
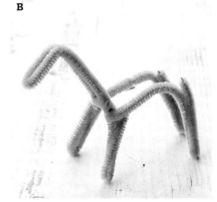

C
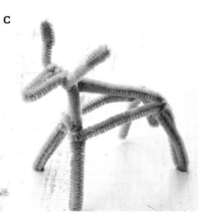

D

WHAT YOU DO

1. Trace patterns, *below*, onto tracing paper and cut out. Cut the 2¼-inch diameter flower with five petals for the narrow pinecone or the same size flower with 10 petals for the shorter wavy pinecone. Cut approximately two flowers of each brown color for a total of 8 to 11 flower shapes for each pinecone. The end of each pinecone requires a smaller flower.

Note: The 5-petal flower doesn't decrease in diameter but each petal is very thin. The 10-petal flower decreases to 1¼ inches; cut two of these.

2. To form ridges on the 5-petal flowers first fold a single petal in half. With needle and thread, hand-stitch the length of the fold, bringing the thread back and forth from one side to the other, stopping ¼ inch before the petal end. Draw the needle back under the sewn ridge and pull it out the center of the flower. Repeat the process with the remaining four petals. Always draw the needle back up to the center. Prepare all the remaining large petals this way. The smallest flower petals are too small to shape; gather them into a single cluster by stitching around the flower center.

3. Simply stitch around the hole and pull the thread tight to gather the fabric. Knot the ends and trim the thread. Repeat the process with all the remaining petals, including the two smallest.

4. Fold the stem in half, wrapping the fold around a round wide highlighter pen (or wooden spoon handle). Twist the ends together where they meet under the pen and then slide it out. Twist a few more inches of wire.

5. For the 5-petal flowers, snip a tiny hole in the center of each flower; the other flowers already have an opening. Bring the floral wire ends together and thread the petals top side first onto the wire. Thread the flowers darkest to lightest, stopping to twist additional wire length as needed. If the fabric coating pulls away, use your wire cutters to cut off the bottom inch or two of the wire. String the specially prepared small

flower on last and then trim the wire ends. It may help to leave ¼ inch of additional wire to prevent the flowers from falling off.

6. Fold the green fabric in half, aligning the fold with the narrow part of the template. Cut out two layers of felt that are connected in the middle. Fold one end of the ribbon and thread it through the wire loop. Slide the loop down to the narrow portion of the felt and then tie the ends together once. Use scissors to snip diagonal slits on either side of the felt. Twist each length of snipped ribbon to give it a more natural appearance.

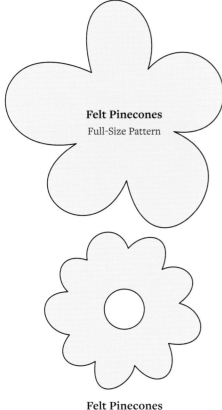

Felt Pinecones
Full-Size Pattern

Felt Pinecones
Full-Size Pattern

Felt Pinecones
Full-Size Pattern

Felt Pinecones
Full-Size Pattern

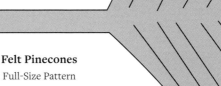

Felt Pinecones
Full-Size Pattern

Bookworm Birds
Shown on page 42

WHAT YOU NEED
Tracing paper
Pencil
Solid-color cardstock
Patterned cardstock
Old paperback book
Glue stick
String

WHAT YOU DO
1. Enlarge and trace bird patterns, *below.* Cut out. With a pencil, trace bird shape onto solid cardstock and wings onto patterned cardstock; cut out.
2. Remove pages from old paperback book. Trace bird and wing shapes onto page and cut out. Glue paperback shapes to matching cardstock shapes; let dry. Trim edges if necessary.
3. Accordion-fold a paperback page, then fold in half to create the bird tail. Glue in place and let dry. Fold wings in half, cut a small slit in the center of the bird, and slide the wings into the slit. Glue into place. Make hanging loop with string and glue to the inside of the wings.

Joy Ornaments
Shown on page 47

WHAT YOU NEED
Typewriter key graphic
Transfer paper
Linen
2½-inch jar lid
Glue; hammer; nail
Black cardstock
Black ⅛-inch ribbon

WHAT YOU DO
1. Download a copyright-free typewriter key graphic and print onto iron-on transfer paper. Iron onto the center of a 4-inch circle of linen. Carefully poke a hole in the top edge of the jar lid with a hammer and nail. Center key design onto the jar lid.
2. Glue the linen to the lid, smoothing the fabric over the top surface and around the edge to the back. Cut a 2½-inch circle of black cardstock and glue to the inside back of the lid. Insert a loop of ribbon through the hole in the jar lid to hang.

Sticks and Stones Wreath
Shown on page 48

WHAT YOU NEED
Fresh green wreath
Stones about 1 to 2 inches in diameter
String
Pinecones
Sticks in various sizes
24-gauge copper wire
2-inch-wide ribbon for hanging wreath
Scissors

WHAT YOU DO
Wire pinecones and wire into wreath as desired. Wrap stones with copper wire and poke into fresh green wreath between pinecones. Wrap string around wreath and poke ends into greens. Slide sticks into wreath around edges. Loop ribbon through wreath top to hang.

Floral Rosettes
Shown on page 46

WHAT YOU NEED
Cardstock: patterns and solids
Glue stick
Matching solid cardstock
1-inch hole punch
Hot-glue gun and glue sticks
Mini self-adhesive letters
Twine

WHAT YOU DO
1. Cut patterned cardstock into twelve 1×6-inch-long strips. Loop each strip in half, patterned side out. Using a glue stick, glue the ends together. Let dry.
2. Punch two circles out of solid cardstock. Using the hot-glue gun, attach the glued ends of the cardstock strips to the center of one circle. Let dry. Glue other circle to other side of strips.
3. Adhere self-adhesive letters to circle front. Loop twine through paper to hang.

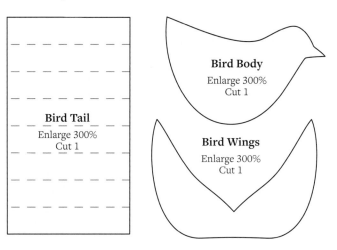

Bird Tail
Enlarge 300%
Cut 1

Bird Body
Enlarge 300%
Cut 1

Bird Wings
Enlarge 300%
Cut 1

Holiday Citrus Garland
Shown on page 44

WHAT YOU NEED
Fresh oranges
Knife
Pinecones
Fresh cranberries
Beads in desired shapes and sizes
Waxed dental floss
Large needle

WHAT YOU DO
Slice the oranges and set aside. Decide on the order of the items to be strung. Thread the needle with dental floss. Thread the items on the floss as desired. Secure the ends by tying or running the needle back and forth through the last item strung.

Paper Cone Pines
Shown on page 49

WHAT YOU NEED
Tracing paper
Printed green scrapbook papers in small organic prints
Scissors
Glue stick or crafts glue for paper
2 clip clothespins
Gold bead

WHAT YOU DO
Enlarge and trace the patterns, *below*, and cut out. Place pattern on the printed paper and cut out. Roll the paper to form a cone and glue in place. Use the clip clothespins on each end to hold the cone until dry. Glue a bead to the top of the tree.

Crystal Topiary
Shown on page 49

WHAT YOU NEED
Crystal plates
Crystal candlesticks
Boxwood leaves
Mercury-glass bird

WHAT YOU DO
Starting at the base, rest a crystal plate on a candlestick. Add a candlestick in the middle of the plate; rest another plate on top of that candlestick. Continue stacking until desired height is achieved. Place boxwood greenery around edges of plates. Add the bird at the top.

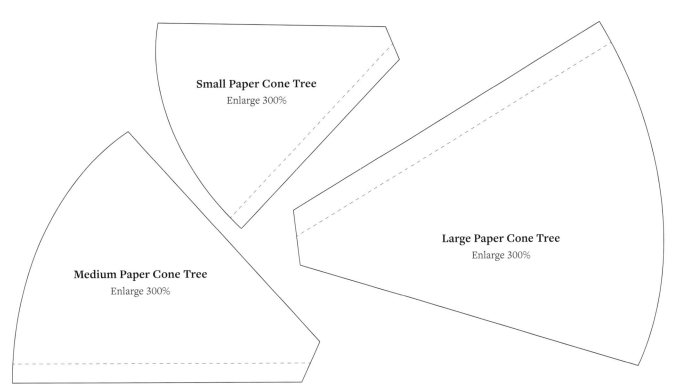

Small Paper Cone Tree
Enlarge 300%

Medium Paper Cone Tree
Enlarge 300%

Large Paper Cone Tree
Enlarge 300%

Naturally Inspired **53**

where treetops
glisten

MAKE THE CENTERPIECE of your holiday decorating your Christmas tree—and make it sparkle with projects you create yourself. Sky blue ornaments with shimmering rhinestones, crystal-laden tree toppers, soft felt trims, and more showcase your evergreen this holiday season.

WINTER CRYSTAL TRIMS
Make the treetops glisten with eye-catching shades of icy blue, snowy white, and frosty silver. Outfit your pine with handmade Winter Crystal Trims and solid blue orbs, then dust the boughs with a generous sprinkling of artificial snow or flocking for an appropriately fluffy finish. For a closer look at the Winter Crystal Trims, see page 59. Instructions for making the crystal ornaments start on page 65.

SPARKLING STAR TRIO Embossed glitter paper and jewels combine with magical paper folding to create a Sparkling Star Trio. The Jeweled 5-Point Star Trim, *opposite*, becomes 3-dimensional when the two patterns are layered. The Elegant 8-Point Star Topper, *below left*, is made with glittering, shimmering cardstock. A Silver Lace Star, *below right*, is layered and folded to make 10 points with jewels at each end. Instructions start on page 66.

Elegant 8-Point Topper

Silver Lace Star

FELT BLUEBIRD ORNAMENTS A symbol of happiness, these Felt Bluebird Ornaments, *opposite* and *right,* are perfect to make and share with friends. These round little birds share the same pattern pieces but can be arranged to create unique resting, flying, or standing poses. Instructions begin on page 64.

WINTER CRYSTAL TRIMS Plain blue matte-finish ornaments become Winter Crystal Trims, *above,* when you embellish them with simple rhinestone patterns. Instructions are on page 65.

JINGLE BELLS RING ORNAMENTS So quick to make, you'll want to make dozens of this clever little ornament! Jingle Bells Ring Ornaments, *above left*, are made using purchased glass ornaments and tiny red jingle bells. Instructions are on page 65.

SIMPLY STAMPED ORNAMENT Tiny stamped prints become the design on a Simply Stamped Ornament, *above right*. Choose your favorite tiny motif to decorate any purchased ornament. Add a dusting of glitter for some holiday sparkle. Instructions are on page 67.

HEARTFELT TRIMS These sweet, hand-embroidered Heartfelt Trims, *above*, will add homespun charm to your tree. No-fray felt is a joy to work with and perfect for beginner sewers. A quick twist of aluminum wire and a simple bead make a lightweight decorative hanger. Use your favorite embroidery stitches to express your love on each unique piece. Instructions begin on page 68. Embroidery stitch diagrams are on page 159.

SATELLITE SNOWFLAKES Striking in their simplicity, Satellite Snowflakes, *opposite*, are reminiscent of 1960s satellite designs. Use a template cutter to make clean, quick circles or use the patterns provided. Hot glue makes quick work of trapping the wire centers and ends between the felt layers. Instructions are on page 71.

TINY BABY SHOE TRIMS Make baby's first Christmas extra special by making a pair of Baby Shoe Trims, *above*. The sweet shoes are made using felt and embroidery stitches and lined with tiny calico prints. A little button flower motif or grosgrain ribbon bows decorate the shoe tops. Instructions start on page 69.

Felt Bluebird Ornaments

Shown on page 59

WHAT YOU NEED

Tracing paper

Pencil

35% nonwoven wool, such as National Nonwovens: light blue, light aqua, pink, white, beige

100% nonwoven wool, such as National Nonwovens: blue and putty

Sewing thread to match fabrics

Embroidery floss: beige, butterceam yellow, aqua, green, dark blue

Off-white twisted silk cord

Pinking shears

Scissors

Straight pins

Sewing needle

Crewel needle

WHAT YOU DO

1. Trace and cut out patterns, *below*. Cut the body and top of the bird wings out of the light blue or aqua felt, the breast out of the pink (or beige), and the under wings out of white or aqua.

2. Cut the smaller circle from the blue felt. Cut out the circle; this is the base piece that the bird is stitched to. Cut the larger circle from the putty felt. Use pinking sheers to cut out the putty felt; set this piece aside until the bird is finished.

3. Play with the arrangement of the pieces, tucking the wings behind and over the body makes a bird at rest. By pulling them out at a diagonal angle the bird appears to be taking off or in flight. Pin the pieces in place and hand-stitch them in place with a sewing needle and thread.

4. Thread a full strand of blue embroidery floss in the crewel needle. Knot the end of the thread and draw the needle up through the underside of your work. Make a French Knot eye, draw the needle back to the backside of the work, tie, and trim the end.

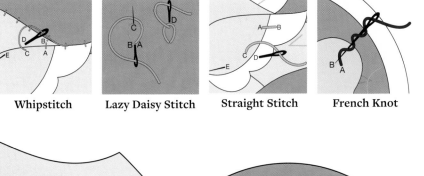

Whipstitch   **Lazy Daisy Stitch**   **Straight Stitch**   **French Knot**

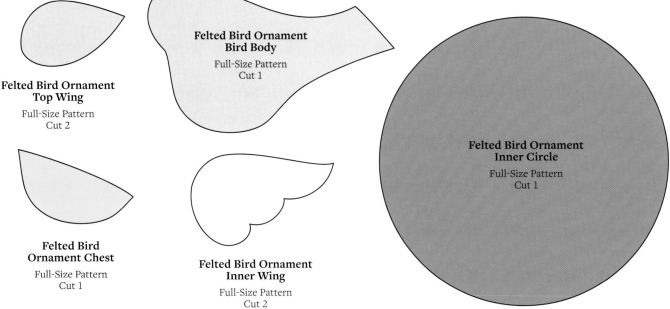

**Felted Bird Ornament
Top Wing**

Full-Size Pattern
Cut 2

**Felted Bird Ornament
Bird Body**

Full-Size Pattern
Cut 1

**Felted Bird
Ornament Chest**

Full-Size Pattern
Cut 1

**Felted Bird Ornament
Inner Wing**

Full-Size Pattern
Cut 2

**Felted Bird Ornament
Inner Circle**

Full-Size Pattern
Cut 1

make the stem. Form a petal or leaf loop at the end of the stem.

8. Use a sewing needle and small invisible stitches to join the edge of the base piece to the putty background.

9. Thread the silk cord into the crewel needle and slip the needle between the felt layers at the top of your ornament. Draw 6 inches of the silk thread through and bring the ends together. Tie them in an overhand knot 3 inches above the felt ornament. Trim both ends 1 inch from the knot.

Jingle Bells Ring Ornaments

Shown on page 60

WHAT YOU NEED

Clear glass ornament
Small red jingle bells
Silver glitter glue
Narrow ribbon

WHAT YOU DO

1. Be sure the ornament is clean and dry. Remove the top from the ornament and set aside. Carefully place jingle bells inside the ornament. Replace the top.

2. Use glitter glue to make dots on the ornament as desired. Let dry. Thread ribbon through top for hanging.

Winter Crystal Trims

Shown on page 59

WHAT YOU NEED

Blue ornaments: round and teardrop
Adhesive gems

WHAT YOU DO

1. Lightly draw pencil lines around the circumferences of the round ornaments and down the sides of the teardrop-shape ornaments.

2. Peel and stick adhesive gems along the lines.

5. Thread the crewel needle with a full strand of buttercream floss to make a beak. Like the eye bring the needle up through the underside; make a V-shape beak with two stitches that are ⅛ inch long. If you're making a standing bird, make two straight stitches out the bottom, cap each one with a horizontal stitch.

6. Thread the crewel needle with a full strand aqua floss. Start making a series of decorative stitches along the wings. Each stitch should span from the lighter underwing to the darker top wing. Make a V-shape stitch in the center of the tail.

7. Using a full strand of green floss, make a couple stitches that slip under the beak to

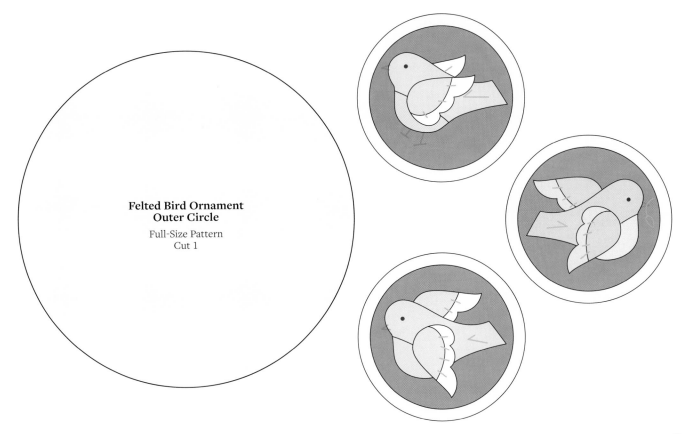

**Felted Bird Ornament
Outer Circle**

Full-Size Pattern
Cut 1

Jeweled 5-Point Star

Elegant 8-Point Topper

Silver Lace Star

Jeweled 5-Point Star
Shown on page 57

WHAT YOU NEED
Tracing paper
Heavy white embossed/glittered paper
White cardstock for punching
Ruler
Pencil
Scissors
Scoring blade
Small circle punch
Assorted jewels
Tissue paper
Fine-tip liquid adhesive

WHAT YOU DO
1. Enlarge and trace star pattern, *below*. Trace around two times on the back side of the paper. Cut out. Use a pencil and ruler to draw score lines on the back side of the

star as shown, connecting each point to the opposite side. Score on each line, scoring the longer lines (on the points) from the back side of the paper to create a "mountain." Score the shorter lines (between the points) from the front side of the paper to create a "valley."
2. Carefully pinch each point to create a dimensional star. Crumple a piece of tissue paper and adhere to the backside of one of the stars to act as a spacer/cushion between the two. Adhere the second star to the tissue paper, arranging so that the points of the second star are visible between the points of the first star.
3. Punch a small circle from white cardstock to fit on the front center point of each star. Adhere a large jewel to each circle using liquid glue. Adhere jewels to the inside of the star points using fine-tipped liquid glue.

Elegant 8-Point Star Topper
Shown on page 56

WHAT YOU NEED
White and cream cardstock (we used shimmery cardstock)
Star pattern (5 stars)
Ruler
Pencil
Scissors
Scoring blade
Embossing folder
Assorted jewels
Fine-tip liquid adhesive

WHAT YOU DO
1. Enlarge and trace three star patterns onto the back side of the white cardstock and two star patterns onto the back side of the cream cardstock, using the pattern, *page 67*. Cut out all five stars. One white star will be left intact and will function as the "base."

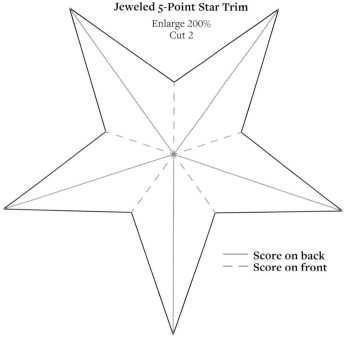

Jeweled 5-Point Star Trim
Enlarge 200%
Cut 2

— Score on back
-- Score on front

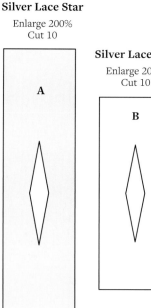

Silver Lace Star
Enlarge 200%
Cut 10

A

Silver Lace Star
Enlarge 200%
Cut 10

B

Silver Lace Star
Enlarge 200%
Cut 10

C

2. From the two cream stars, cut out the eight small diamond-shape pieces referring to Pattern A, *below*. Emboss and adhere four to the front side of the "base" star and four to the back.

3. From the remaining two white stars, cut four longer diamond-shape pieces referring to Pattern B, *below*, and four medium-shaped pieces, referring to Pattern C, *below*. With a ruler and pencil, draw a line on the back side of each from tip to tip, then carefully score. Bend slightly to create dimension, then adhere four of the diamonds to the front side of the star and four to the back.

4. Use liquid glue to adhere jewels to the center and points of each side of the star.

Silver Lace Star
Shown on page 56

WHAT YOU NEED
Heavy glittery cardstock/paper in
   2–3 patterns (single- or double-sided)
Scissors
Scoring blade
Circle punch
Assorted jewels
Fine-tip liquid adhesive
Very strong double-sided tape, such as
   Tacky Tape or Scor Tape

WHAT YOU DO
Note: Our star has 10 points, but yours may have fewer or more, depending on how you score and adhere the pieces. The instructions shown here are for a 10-point star.

Cutting the Patterns

1. From Patterned Paper #1, cut 10 strips, each 1½×6 inches. Score at 3 inches, then while folded, cut a triangle along the fold. (When the strip is unfolded, the hole will be diamond-shaped.) See Pattern A, *opposite*. From Patterned Paper #2, cut 10 strips, each 1½×4 inches. Score at 2 inches, then while folded, cut a triangle along the fold. See Pattern B, *opposite*. From Patterned Paper #1, cut 10 strips, each 1½×3 inches. Score at 1½ inches then while folded, cut a triangle along the fold. See Pattern C, *opposite*.

2. Each point of the star will be created from a 6-inch, 4-inch, and 3-inch strip. With the patterned side of the paper to the inside, fold each of the strips and adhere together along the short edges with very strong adhesive. Do this for each of the 10 sets of strips. Each "point" of the snowflake star will resemble a triangle with three layers.

3. Adhere each of the "points" together: Place strong tape along the flat sides of the 6-inch strips. Adhere each point to the next until they are all adhered together in a star formation.

4. Punch a circle from patterned paper and adhere to the center of the star on each side. Adhere a large jewel to the circle using liquid glue. Use a fine-tip liquid adhesive to adhere jewels to the tips of the snowflake points as desired.

Simply Stamped Ornament
Shown on page 60

WHAT YOU NEED
Matte-finish glass ornament
Small towel
Disposable plate
Glass paint
Small stamp
Glitter

WHAT YOU DO
1. Be sure the ornament is clean and dry. Lay the ornament on the towel to keep stable. Place a small amount of paint on the disposable plate. Using just a little paint, stamp the ornament by rolling it over the surface. Dust with glitter. Let dry. Repeat for the other side.

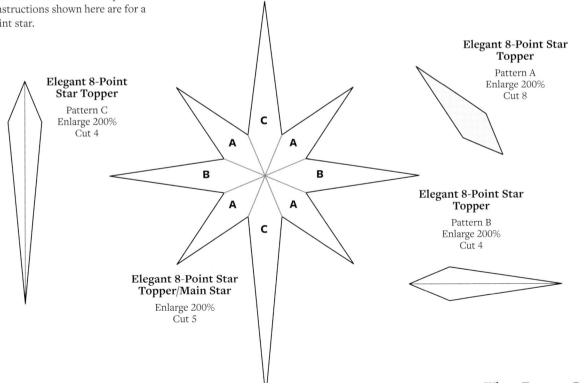

Elegant 8-Point Star Topper
Pattern C
Enlarge 200%
Cut 4

Elegant 8-Point Star Topper
Pattern A
Enlarge 200%
Cut 8

Elegant 8-Point Star Topper
Pattern B
Enlarge 200%
Cut 4

Elegant 8-Point Star Topper/Main Star
Enlarge 200%
Cut 5

Heartfelt Trims
Full-Size Patterns

Happy

Love

OXO
XOX

XOX
OXO

Heartfelt Trims
Shown on page 61

WHAT YOU NEED
Tracing paper
35% wool felt, such as National
   Nonwovens: fuchsia, red, light pink
Embroidery floss: red, light green, yellow
Pink sewing thread
Polyester fiber stuffing
12-gauge aluminum wire
½-inch round wood beads
Scissors; pinking sheers
Sewing needle; crewel needle
Sewing machine
Wire cutters
Round nose pliers

WHAT YOU DO
1. Trace patterns, *left,* and cut out.
Cut the three heart templates out of three
different colors of felt. Make a decorative
edge by trimming the smallest and largest
hearts with pinking sheers.
2. Use a full strand of embroidery floss in
your crewel needle to stitch a message on
the smallest heart. Start and end all
stitching on the back side to hide the
knots. Use an elongated cross-stitch and
boxy circle to make a hugs and kisses.
Letters can also be stitched with just a few
connected stitches. Stitch letters with
three to four letter words like Love, Mom,
hugs, etc. Embellish the message with a
simple Lazy Daisy flower or two green
petals to form a leaf cluster.

3. Stack the hearts, largest at the bottom
and smallest at the top. Pin the three
hearts together. Starting at the base of the
heart, machinestitch around the inside
edge of the smallest (top) heart. Stop 2
inches from the base of the heart. Lift the
presser foot; fold back the last (biggest)
heart. Reset the presser foot and continue
stitching. This will give a continuous stitch
on the front of the heart but leaves an
opening on the backside to stuff the heart.
4. Poke polyester fiberfill into the opening
at the back of the heart. Hand-stitch the
opening closed.
5. Cut a 6-inch length of wire. Starting
with one end of the wire, spiral it a couple
of times around the pliers. Thread a bead
onto the wire. Repeat the process to make
a smaller spiral at the other wire end,
switching the spiraling directions to form
an S shape.
6. Hand-stitch the small end of the hanger
to the center front of the heart.

Tiny Baby-Shoe Trims
Shown on page 63

For the Cream Shoes
WHAT YOU NEED
Tracing paper
Pencil
1 12×12-inch piece of cream felt
Iron-on interfacing
Scrap of coordinating tiny-print fabric for
   lining of cream baby shoe
Dark red embroidery floss to match fabric
8 inches of 1-inch-wide dark red ribbon

WHAT YOU DO
1. Trace the patterns, *pages 70–71,* and cut
out. Layer the three layers of fabric, felt,
and interfacing, and pin in place. Cut shoe
pattern, upper and sole, from all three
pieces at once. Lay felt pieces aside. Iron
interfacing to fabric using a warm iron.
2. Put fabric/interfacing sole and upper
together with the felt so there are three

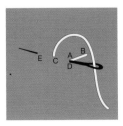
Backstitch

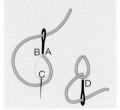
Lazy Daisy Stitch

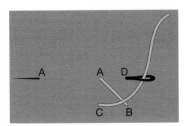
Cross-Stitch

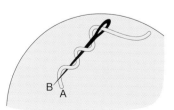
French Knot

layers of fabric. Zigzag around edges of sole and bottom of upper. Sew back opening of upper with the felt sides together, fabric out. Zigzag over this also. Stitch closed toe of upper. With fabric facing out on sole and upper, pin upper to sole. Zigzag around the bottom edge of the shoe. Turn inside out.

3. With embroidery floss, sew a casting stitch around the opening of the shoe. Tie the ribbon into a bow and stitch to the tongue of the shoe.

For the Pink Shoes

WHAT YOU NEED
Tracing paper
Pencil
1 12×12-inch piece of pink felt
Iron-on interfacing
Scrap of coordinating tiny-print fabric for lining of pink baby shoe
Cream embroidery floss to match fabric
Green embroidery floss to match fabric
2 small cream buttons

WHAT YOU DO
1. Trace patterns, *below and opposite*, and cut out. Layer the three layers of fabric, felt and interfacing and pin in place. Cut shoe pattern, upper and sole, from all three pieces at once. Lay felt pieces aside. Iron interfacing to fabric using a warm iron.

2. Put fabric/interfacing sole and upper together with the felt so there are three layers of fabric. Zigzag around edges of sole and bottom of upper. Sew back opening of upper with the felt sides together, fabric

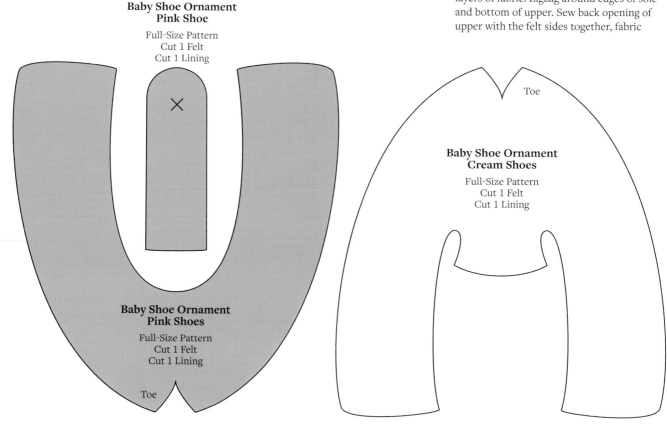

**Baby Shoe Ornament
Pink Shoe**

Full-Size Pattern
Cut 1 Felt
Cut 1 Lining

**Baby Shoe Ornament
Pink Shoes**

Full-Size Pattern
Cut 1 Felt
Cut 1 Lining

Toe

**Baby Shoe Ornament
Cream Shoes**

Full-Size Pattern
Cut 1 Felt
Cut 1 Lining

Toe

out. Zigzag over this also. Stitch closed toe of upper.

3. With fabric facing out on sole and upper, pin upper to sole. Zigzag around the bottom edge of the shoe. Turn inside out. With the cream embroidery floss, sew a casting stitch around the opening of the shoe. Sew a tiny button to the mouth/opening of the shoe

4. With green embroidery floss sew three tiny leaves around the button. Pin the shoe strap to the side of the shoe and make a stitch to hold it in place. Stitch the other tiny button over the stitch.

Satellite Snowflakes
Shown on page 62

WHAT YOU NEED
Tracing paper
Silver wire floral stem
35% wool felt, such as National
    Nonwovens: light blue, aqua, white
Patterns or circle template (tiny
    circles are from the insides of flower
    templates)or die cut (optional)
Hot-glue gun and glue sticks
Pinking sheers
Wire cutters

WHAT YOU DO
1. Trace the circle patterns, *below*, to cut multiple layers of felt into 1½-inch, 1¼-inch, ⅞-inch, and ⅜-inch circles. The tiny ⅜-inch dots are the cut-out centers of flowers. Continue cutting until you have a

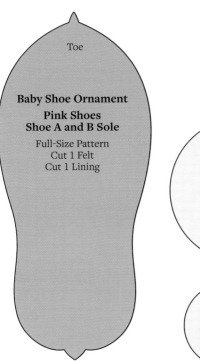

Baby Shoe Ornament

Pink Shoes
Shoe A and B Sole

Full-Size Pattern
Cut 1 Felt
Cut 1 Lining

Toe

generous stacks of different sizes and colored circles. Or use a die cut.

2. Use wire cutters to divide each silver floral stem into three 6-inch long sections.

Note: You'll need four 6-inch wires for each snowflake.

3. Using the hot-glue gun, squeeze a drop of glue into the center of a felt circle (1¼-inch or ⅞-inch). Place the wire end

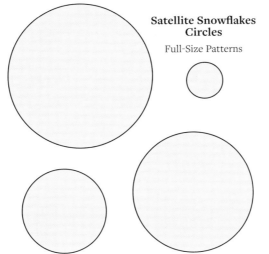

Satellite Snowflakes Circles

Full-Size Patterns

over the glue and then place a second circle over the first trapping the wire between the layers. Repeat the process to cover the other wire end and both ends of the three remaining wires.

4. Place the center of all four wires over the center of a 1½-inch felt circle. Position two of the wires to form an X and the other two to form a + sign. Hot-glue a second 1½-inch circle over the first, trapping the positioned wire centers in between the felt layers.

5. Hot-glue pairs of circles to the center of the exposed wires halfway between the center circle and the circle ends.

6. Use pinking sheers to trim two 1½-inch circles. Hot-glue these decorative circles to either side of the center circle. Continue stacking and gluing smaller circles to decorative circles.

7. Hot-glue smaller contrasting circles (light on dark or dark on light) to the center of the smaller circles in the middle and end of the wires. Let cool.

'twas the
night before
christmas

ALL THROUGH THE HOUSE, there isn't a creature stirring—or is there? The excitement of the big day and the spirit of Christmas can be felt in every room of the house. Make this amazing night even more magical by creating crafts and decorations to share.

'TWAS THE NIGHT BEFORE CHRISTMAS TREE
Fill your evergreen with images from Clement Clarke Moore's poem, *'Twas the Night Before Christmas.* Miniature nightcaps and blankets, sugarplum cookies, miniature story books, and a family of wool mice nestle in the tree waiting for Christmas morning. Take a closer look at all of the ornaments beginning on page 76.

OLD-FASHIONED SWEATER
STOCKINGS Old-Fashioned
Sweater Stockings, *opposite*, are
hung by the chimney with care.
Make them yourself using
castaway sweaters in rich vintage
colors. Choose sweaters with
cables and interesting pockets
so the stockings have instant
personality. Then add little
embellishments to finish each
one. Instructions begin on
page 82.

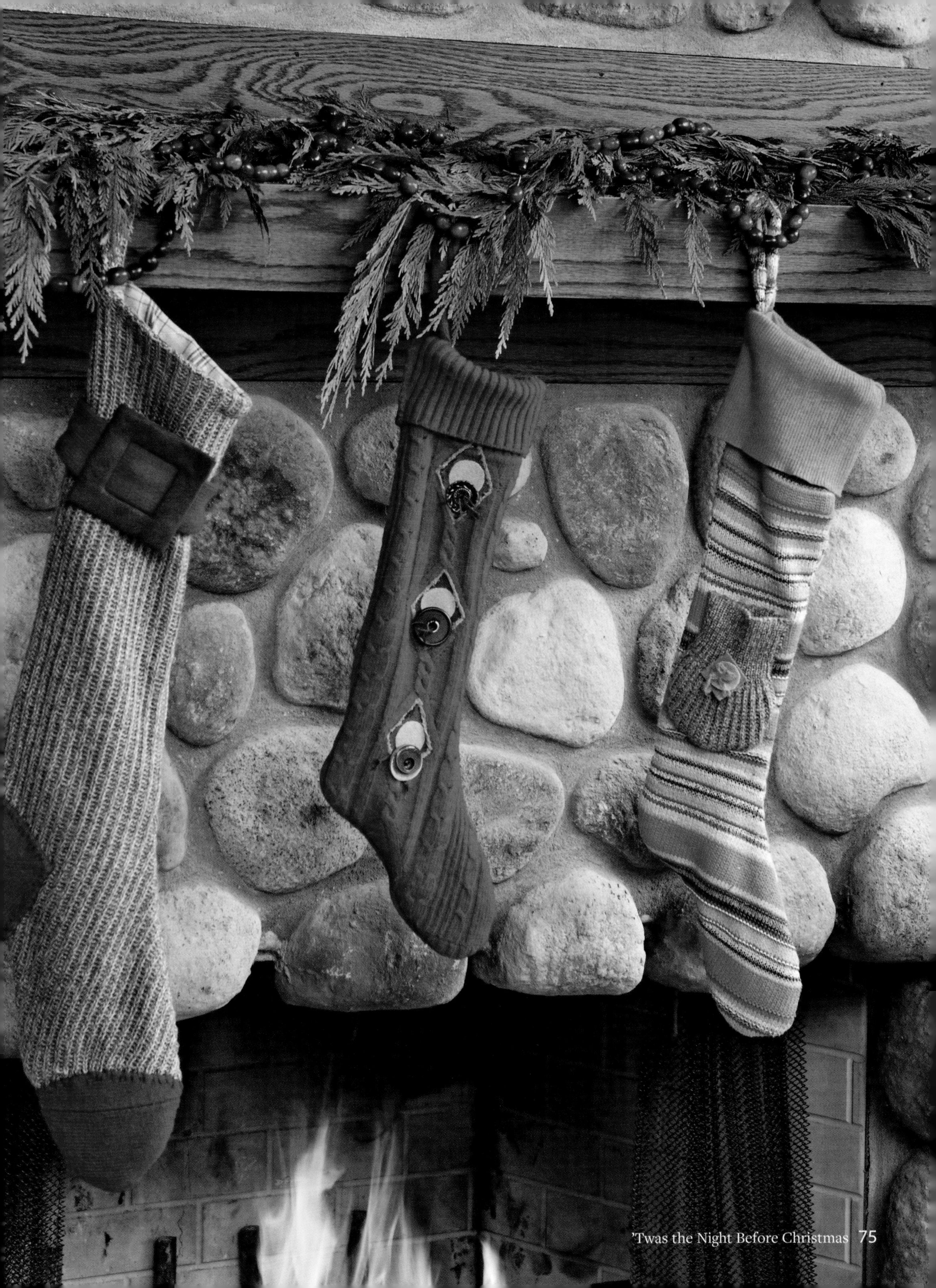

NIGHT BEFORE CHRISTMAS MOUSE FAMILY Tiny little mice—each with his or her own adorable personality—adorn the tree just waiting for the big day. The needle-felted mice are made from wool roving with tiny accessories made from fabric and paper scraps. The baby mouse, *above*, snuggles in a walnut shell. For instructions on how to needle felt and instructions for how to make this sweet little family, see page 84.

TINY BOOK ORNAMENTS, *above left*, tell the story of "'Twas the Night Before Christmas." The books are really mini versions of a vintage book with parchment paper pages and a ribbon for hanging. Instructions are on page 85.

LITTLE VINTAGE NIGHTCAP ORNAMENTS, *above right*, hang on the tree waiting for St. Nicholas to arrive. The little hats are made from discarded T-shirt fabric and each has its own personality. Instructions are on page 86.

TINY BLANKET ORNAMENTS Tuck these Tiny Blanket Ornaments, *above left*, in your tree while you dream of sugarplums. The blankets are made from T-shirt fabric in colorful prints. The pillows attach with just a little stitch to secure. Instructions are on page 86.

SANTA'S BUCKLE WRAPS Wrap special packages with a quick and clever buckle bow to mirror Santa's tummy—like a bowl full of jelly. Vintage buckles are used here, but any buckle will work. Instructions are on page 87.

ADVENT COOKIES AND DECORATED JAR Make the night and the days before Christmas memorable by starting an Advent tradition in your home this year. It is so easy and such fun to create Advent Cookies and Decorated Jar for the whole family to enjoy. The cookies are wood cutouts handsomely painted and decorated. Each day one goes on the tree. A sweet poem goes with the activity. Instructions for making the ornaments and the jar are on page 87. The poem is on page 89.

to:

Old-Fashioned Sweater Stockings
Shown on page 75

WHAT YOU NEED
Tracing paper
Pencil
Old sweaters to cut up
Scissors
Matching thread
⅓ yard cotton fabric for lining

FOR LARGE STOCKING
3½-inch square of cardboard
3½-inch square of thin cotton batting
5-inch square of brown suedelike fabric
Scraps of fusible interfacing for
    heel/toe pieces
3×13½-inch piece of contrast sweater
    fabric for belt
Scraps of contrast sweater fabric
    for heel/toe pieces
Brown embroidery floss
Hot glue gun; glue sticks

FOR MEDIUM-SIZE STOCKING:
Cuff and bottom of sleeve from
    contrasting sweater for pocket
Scraps of felted wool or sweaters for
    pocket
Embellishments
Coordinating yarn
Two 5×7¼-inch pieces contrasting sweater
    fabric for cuff, cut with one long edge of
    each piece from finished sweater edges

FOR SMALL STOCKING:
Scraps of felted wool and brown
    suedelike fabric for embellishments on
    stocking front
Scraps of contrasting color yarn
Three 1¼-inch brown buttons
Fabric glue
Brown embroidery floss

WHAT YOU DO
1. Enlarge and trace patterns, *below* and *page 83,* and cut out. With right sides together, cut two of the stocking patterns from each of the sweater fabrics and cotton

lining fabrics. Small stocking is cut with top edge of stocking at top of turtleneck sweater edge so that finished edge of ribbing folds over to make the cuff. Cut a 2×7-inch strip for hanging loops. (Hint: Because the sweater fabrics are so stretchy when cut, it is helpful to sew seams using an even feed foot on the sewing machine, reduce pressure on the presser foot, and lengthen the stitch to help stocking keep its shape.)

For the Large Stocking
Iron interfacing onto back of heel and toe sweater pieces. Press seam allowances to back along interfacing edges. Place on right side of stocking front and stitch in place with three strands brown embroidery floss, making large irregular straight stitches over the edges of the patches and through sweater fabric. Stitch stocking front to back along the side and lower edges, with right sides together and ½-inch seam allowance. Turn right side out and press. Stitch lining pieces together in the same manner. Fold loop piece right sides together and stitch in ¼-inch seam along long edge. Turn right side out. Pin loop to outside side edge of stocking, with top raw edges even. Put stocking inside lining, having right sides together. Stitch around top edges in ½-inch seam, leaving an opening for turning. Pull lining through opening and then inside stocking. Press top edge and slip-stitch opening closed. Cut open square shape from cardboard and batting for buckle. Layer batting onto cardboard. Place wrong side of brown fabric over this and fold edges to the back, gluing in place with hot-glue gun. Cut out center opening from brown square of fabric, leaving seam allowances to fold to the back and glue in place. For belt, fold contrasting piece of sweater in half with long edges together. Stitch with ¼-inch

**Medium Stocking
Pocket Embellishment**
Enlarge 400%
Cut 1

**Medium Stocking
Pocket Embellishment**
Enlarge 400%
Cut 1

**Medium Stocking
Pocket**
Enlarge 400%
Cut 1 from sweater sleeve

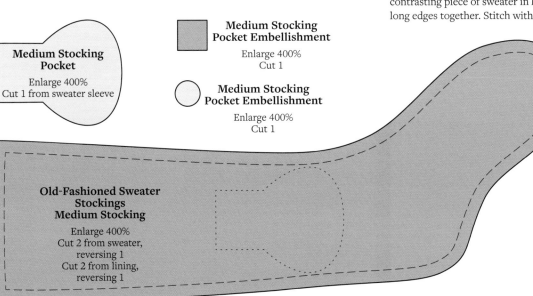

**Old-Fashioned Sweater
Stockings
Medium Stocking**
Enlarge 400%
Cut 2 from sweater,
reversing 1
Cut 2 from lining,
reversing 1

seam. Turn right side out. Loop belt around stocking top edge about 3 inches from the top. Hand-stitch ends together at center back of stocking. Place buckle on top of belt and hand-stitch in place using invisible stitches just under buckle side edges.

For the Medium Stocking

Cut sleeve of coordinating sweater to match pattern, with ribbing cuff at top. With right sides together, stitch bottom edge together in ¼-inch seam. Turn right side out and press. Add trims to front of pocket, making running stitches with pink yarn around the front just under the ribbing. Add shapes to center of pocket and sew yarn in center of shapes. Tie yarn in bow. Hand-stitch pocket in place on stocking front. With right sides together, stitch around side and lower edges of the stocking, leaving top edges open, using

½-inch seam allowance. Clip curves, turn sweater stocking pieces right side out, and press. Stitch lining pieces together in the same manner. With right sides together, sew long edge of loop piece together. Turn right side out. With right sides together, sew short side of cuff piece to form a circular tube. Place hanging loop down inside stocking at side edge with raw edges at top edge of stocking. Insert lining inside stocking sweater piece, with wrong sides together and top edges even. Baste through all layers of stocking, lining, and loop. Insert cuff inside stocking, with right side of cuff against the right side of the stocking lining. Sew around top edge through all layers using a ½-inch seam. Flip cuff piece out over front of stocking. Using thread to match the cuff, tack the cuff to the stocking by sewing stitches through both layers at the side seams.

For the Small Stocking

Glue embellished shapes onto stocking front as desired. Glue yarn trim around outside edge of trim to further define. Sew buttons over shapes using three strands brown embroidery floss and knotting thread at the front. Leave 1-inch tails to floss. With right sides together stitch stocking front to back around side and lower edges, using ½-inch seam allowance. Clip curves, turn, and press. Stitch lining pieces together in the same manner. With right sides together, stitch long edge of loop in ¼-inch seam. Turn right side out. Place loop at top side edge of stocking and pin in place. Fold ½-inch seam allowance to inside along top edge of lining. Insert lining into stocking, with wrong sides together. Hand- stitch lining to top edge of stocking.

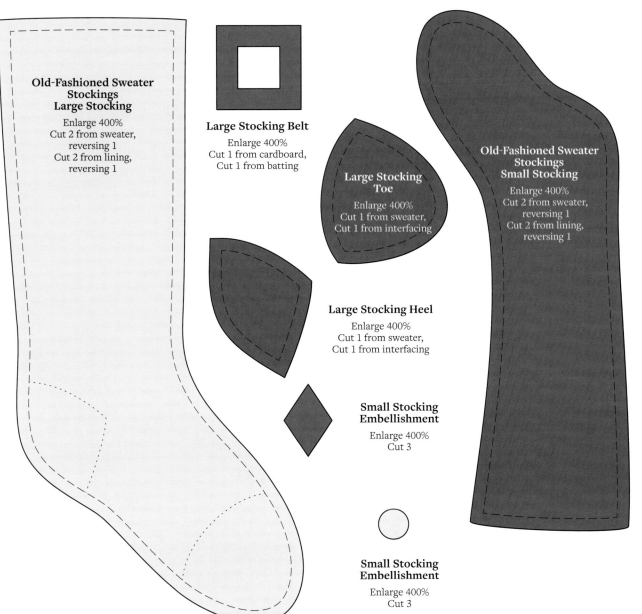

Old-Fashioned Sweater Stockings Large Stocking

Enlarge 400%
Cut 2 from sweater, reversing 1
Cut 2 from lining, reversing 1

Large Stocking Belt

Enlarge 400%
Cut 1 from cardboard,
Cut 1 from batting

Large Stocking Toe

Enlarge 400%
Cut 1 from sweater,
Cut 1 from interfacing

Large Stocking Heel

Enlarge 400%
Cut 1 from sweater,
Cut 1 from interfacing

Small Stocking Embellishment

Enlarge 400%
Cut 3

Small Stocking Embellishment

Enlarge 400%
Cut 3

Old-Fashioned Sweater Stockings Small Stocking

Enlarge 400%
Cut 2 from sweater, reversing 1
Cut 2 from lining, reversing 1

Night Before Christmas Mouse Family

Shown on page 76–77

WHAT YOU NEED

Wool roving in various natural colors: browns, caramel, creme, grey

Felting foam pad

Felting needle—38-gauge is a good all-purpose needle for general felting and detail work

Fabric scraps in various small prints such as seersucker teal and white stripe, and a cotton green polka dot and green stripe

Scissors

Needle

Thread

Small embellishments such as tiny packages, ribbon, etc.

Embroidery thread

WHAT YOU DO

To Build the Mouse Body

1. Start each part of the mouse with a tuft of wool: 3 inches in diameter for making the body; 2 inches in diameter for the head; 1 inch diameter for the ears, and about 1½ inches in diameter for the arms and legs. *See Photo A.* Felt each piece separately and attach later.

2. Roll the roving around in the palm of your hand until it becomes compact. *See Photo B.*

3. How felting works: Each time the needle pokes through the felt and is brought out, the wool gets compacted. Tiny barbs on the side of the special felting needle ensnare and interlock the wool fibers. It is a long process to compact the fibers enough to start getting shapes; the needle will go in and out hundreds of times to get a desired firmness. Felting is a little like sculpting. But instead of clay you use wool; instead of your fingers you use the needle.

Place the compacted roving onto the felting foam pad. Use the needles to poke and shape the wool. *See Photo C.*

4. To attach pieces together (arm/legs/head to body), position the pieces together. Poke the needle through both pieces at an angle to ensnare fibers together from each of the pieces you want conjoined. Add a small amount of wool over the tops of the "seams" to cover the area where the two pieces are joined. *See Photo D.*

5. For ears, make tiny needle-felted pieces. *See Photo E.* Attach to the head using the felting needle. *See Photo F.*

6. For eyes, nose, teeth, and mouth, take tiny (less than ⅛-inch pieces) of wool in black for the eyes, pink for the nose, white for teeth, black for mouth and roll them between your fingers. Use the needle to attach. *See Photo G.*

7. For the mouse tail, roll a piece of tufted wool into a long "tube" between your

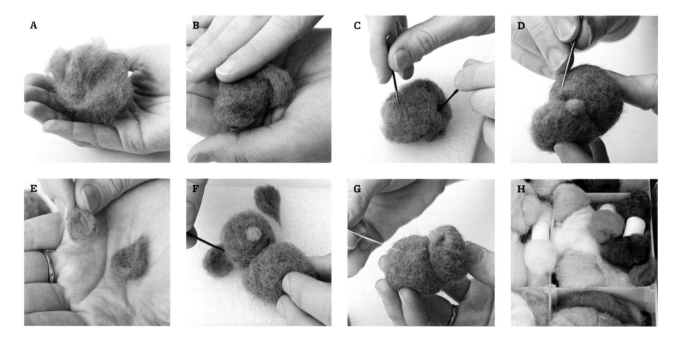

fingers. On the felting pad, poke at the rolled felt until it is compacted. Attach to mouse body with felting needle.

8. To "color" mouse cheeks and inside of mouse ears in pink, take a tiny amount of pink wool, spread over area you want colorized, and attach with needle.

Note: A little bit of pink goes a long way. Wool roving comes in a variety of colors. *See Photo H.*

To Create Mouse Accessories

1. Create mouse accessories after the mouse has been felted. To make hat, cut two triangles out of desired fabric. Join wrong sides together. Attach sleep cap with thread to felted mouse. Fold sleep cap over and sew through the layers to hold the fold you create. For baby blanket, simply wrap a tiny scrap of fabric around the mouse. Purchase small package or stocking or make from paper and felt. Glue to mouse.

2. To attach hanging loop, use a needle with larger eye; thread the embroidery thread for loop through the top of the mouse head through the backside. Tie a bow/knot at the top from thread ends.

Tiny Book Ornaments
Shown on page 78

WHAT YOU NEED
Copy of vintage image or similar copyright
 free graphic reduced to 2¾×3⅝ inches
6×4-inch piece of cardstock in desired color
Scissors
4 pieces of 6×4-inch parchment paper
Crafts glue
Narrow ribbon

WHAT YOU DO
1. Copy and cut out book front, *right.* Glue to solid-color cardstock on right side. Fold in half. Fold parchment paper in half and glue each one to crease in center.

2. Glue ribbon at inside crease for hanger. Let dry.

Tiny Book Ornament

Little Vintage Nightcap Ornaments

Shown on page 78

WHAT YOU NEED

Tracing paper

Pencil

Scraps of single-knit or thin sweater knit fabrics from discarded T-shirts

Matching sewing thread

Perle cotton thread

WHAT YOU DO

1. Trace pattern, *opposite*, onto tracing paper and cut out. Cut two from nightcap pattern, placing front opening edge along finished ribbed or hemmed edge of garment. With right sides together, stitch long side edges together in ¼-inch seam. Turn and press.

2. Cut a length of perle cotton and wrap securely around narrow end of nightcap, about 1 inch from end. Knot thread tightly to draw end together and cut thread to leave short tails. Cut fringe at end of cap, clipping from cut end in to where string is wrapped around.

3. Fold long tail of cap over to make desired shape, taking a few stitches through fabric to anchor in place. Sew perle cotton length at top edge of cap for a hanging loop.

Tiny Blanket Ornaments

Shown on page 79

WHAT YOU NEED

Scissors

Scraps single-knit fabric from discarded T-shirts

Matching sewing thread

Perle cotton

Small amount polyfil stuffing

WHAT YOU DO

1. Cut scraps of fabric to measurements indicated on quilt diagrams, *below*. Stitch pieces together using ¼-inch seams. Cut backing fabric to 4½×6½ inches. With right sides together, stitch blanket front to back, leaving an opening for turning. Clip corners, turn, and press. Hand stitch opening closed. Tie quilt as desired, using one or two strands of perle cotton thread.

2. Make pillow by cutting fabric to 3½×4½ inches. With right sides together, fold fabric in half to measure 3½×2 ¼ inches. Stitch around outside edges using ¼-inch seam, leaving an opening for turning. Clip corner, turn, and press. Add small piece of stuffing inside. Hand-stitch opening closed. Flip corners of quilt and arrange pillow as desired. Secure pillow to quilt with a couple invisible hand stitches. Using perle cotton, stitch a length at the top center edge and knot in place to make a hanging loop.

Tiny Blanket Ornaments

Full-Size Patterns

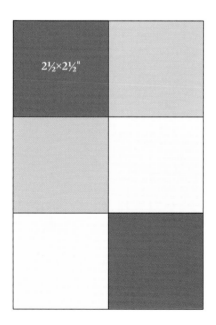

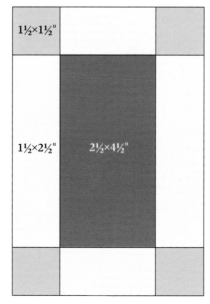

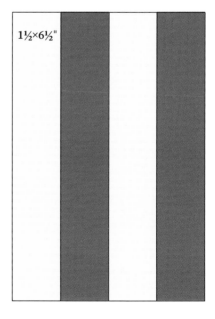

Advent Cookies and Decorated Jar

Shown on page 80

WHAT YOU NEED FOR COOKIES

25 purchased wood shapes resembling cutout cookies or thin wood to cut out cookie cutter shapes
Cookie cutters (if making own shapes)
Band saw (if making own shapes)
Fine sandpaper (if making own shapes)
Small drill
Tan acrylic paint
Ink, such as Distress Ink for shading cookies
Fine glitter
White glue suitable for glitter
Fabric paint with fine-tip applicator (in coordinating colors)
Pearl paint, such as Liquid Pearls
Cardstock
Brayer
Computer/printer/stamps for numbers
Ribbon or twine

WHAT YOU DO

1. *If making own shapes,* draw around cookie cutters onto thin wood and cut out using band saw. Sand edges until smooth. Or, use purchased precut wood pieces (available at crafts stores).

2. Drill a hole in the top of the wood shapes. Paint both sides of wood shapes and allow to dry. Decorate as desired to resemble cookies, using glitter to resemble sugar and fabric paint to resemble frosting. Use dots of pearl paint to resemble dragees. Let dry. See *page 88* for ideas.

3. For a layered cookie look, trace and cut slightly smaller shapes from cardstock to create "frosting." Adhere the cardstock "frosting" with white glue and use brayer to smooth.

4. Print or stamp small numbers 1 to 25 to fit the back of cookies to represent each day of Advent. Adhere to the back of each cookie in desired order. The numbers correspond to the verses in the poem. **Note:** You might wish to designate a special cookie for December 25. To do the activity, read one verse each day, *page 89*, and hang a cookie on the tree each day of Advent.

WHAT YOU NEED FOR JAR

Large clear jar to hold cookies
Patterned paper and coordinating cardstock
Red cardstock
White cardstock
Scissors
Strong tape adhesive, such as Tacky Tape
Crafts glue
Scalloped shape die cut (optional)
Graphics for label: Computer lettering or alphabet stickers; mouse sticker, drawing, or copyright free image
Foam adhesive dots
Ribbon

WHAT YOU DO FOR JAR

1. Cut strips of patterned paper to fit around jar; mat with a strip of cardstock and tape securely to jar.

2. For jar label, cut a large circle from colored cardstock to fit jar; cut a smaller circle from white cardstock. Add a scalloped edge if desired using a shaped die cut. Layer and glue together. Draw or add a sticker or copyright free image of a mouse to the top portion of the circle and lettering that reads, "The Mice Before Christmas." Add other words as desired.

3. For lid, cut a large circle adding a slightly smaller scalloped circle from cardstock if desired; cut a smaller circle from a matching patterned paper. Adhere to lid. Fill jar with Advent ornaments. Tie ribbon around jar lid.

Santa's Buckle Wraps

Shown on page 87

WHAT YOU NEED

Wrapped package
Vintage or new buckles
Wide ribbon
Crafts glue or tape

WHAT YOU DO:

Slide ribbon through buckle leaving enough extra ribbon on both sides to tuck under lid or tape to underside of box. Adhere to hold. Add purchased or handmade gift tag.

Nightcap Ornament
Full-Size Pattern
Cut 1 back,
Cut 1 front,
(add ¼" seam allowance
to front sides only)

Advent Cookies

Design Ideas

The Mice Before Christmas

An Advent Christmas Cookie Activity
written by Janet Petersma
Poem based on *'Twas the Night Before Christmas*
by Clement C. Moore

Day 1. "It's the night before Christmas!" cried dear Mama Mouse.
Sweet scents from the oven drifted all through the house.

Day 2. Three baby mice crept to the kitchen with care
Hoping to find some delicious crumbs there.

Day 3. They should have been nestled all snug in their beds,
But visions of gingerbread danced in their heads!

Day 4. Mama in her nutshell, Papa in his cap
Had just curled up tight for a Christmas Eve nap.

Day 5. When out of the kitchen, they heard such a clatter
They hopped out of bed to see what was the matter.

Day 6. Away to the kitchen they ran in a flash.
They peeked in the doorway, then heard a loud crash!

Day 7. Great clouds of flour, like new fallen snow,
Spilled from a bowl to the oak floor below!

Day 8. Then what to their now worried eyes should appear
But their littlest mouse—cookie dough ear to ear!

Day 9. His sister was climbing, so lively and quick,
Up to the top of a tall candlestick!

Day 10. She jumped in the dough, in a Christmas Eve game
With squeals of delight, as Mama called her name.

Day 11. "A cookie with sprinkles! And gingerbread too!"
And white frosting coated her feet just like glue!

Day 12. The third baby mouse, quite furry and small,
cried "Warm sugar cookies! YUM! Nibbles for all!"

Day 13. As Mama looked on with increasing dread,
He climbed on a cookie and rode like a sled.

Day 14. Straight down the pile of white flour he flew,
His nose caked in sugar and green frosting too!

Day 15. And then in a twinkling, a gingerbread man
Jumped up and took the young mouse by the hand.

Day 16. They danced to the plate where a Christmas tree lay.
"Stand up, Christmas tree!" they heard Gingerbread say.

Day 17. The tree cookie rose, all shiny and bright,
And waltzed 'round the plate with a snowman so white.

Day 18. Then Gingerbread Man took the three mice on his back.
They woke all the cookies that cooled on the rack.

Day 19. The sugar—it sparkled with colors so merry!
The pink frosting glistened! It tasted like cherry!

Day 20. Sweet snowflake cookies pranced all in a row,
With candy jewels glittering, white as the snow.

Day 21. The littlest mouse held a bow in his teeth
And placed it atop of a green cookie wreath.

Day 22. The sister mouse watched with her full little belly
From high up on top of a big jar of jelly.

Day 23. The cookies danced on—the kitchen a mess!
Who would clean up? It was anyone's guess!

Day 24. Then Gingerbread Man smiled and nodded his head,
So Mama Mouse knew she had nothing to dread.

Day 25. He spoke not a word, but gathered his crew.
They cleaned up the kitchen— every crumb too!
He waved to the mice, wiped the little one's fur,
Then the cookies lay down on the trays where they were.
"It's past time for bed, dears! Come along now!"
Called tired Mama Mouse while Papa wiped his brow.
"The cookies! They danced!" squealed the mice with delight.
The mice, before Christmas, had a magical night!

all is calm
all is white

BRING THE WINTER WONDERLAND INSIDE with the crafts and decorations you make—all in snowy white. Felt ivory blooms on a pillow, silver white jewels on a tree, and a collection of vintage buttons on a greeting all share the beauty of a simply beautiful white Christmas.

WINTER WHITE WREATH
Mimic snow-covered nature with a
Winter White Wreath that you make
using a pinecone wreath and a simple
reindeer figurine. The wreath is simply
spray-painted with ivory paint.
Instructions are on page 98.

JEWELRY BROOCH PACKAGE TOPPER Make your packages twinkle like snowflakes by adding vintage jewelry trims to make a Jewelry Brooch Package Topper, *opposite*. Instructions are on page 98.

SPARKLING PEACE LETTERS Scrapbook papers, chipboard letters, and shimmering rhinestones combine to make Sparkling Peace Letters, *above*, for your holiday mantel. The purchased letters are embellished with cut-out shapes of textured white scrapbook papers and highlighted with jewels. Instructions are on page 99.

CENTERPIECE IN WHITE Pretty tumblers become containers to hold all things white. Create the Centerpiece in White, *left*, using creamy and white items such as ornaments, candy, and acrylic snowflakes. Instructions are on page 98.

CHRISTMAS NOEL MESSAGE Vintage buttons add texture and subtle shades of white to a Christmas Noel Message, *below*. Chipboard is painted and decorated to spell the holiday greeting. Instructions are on page 99.

JEWELED TREES Covered with pearls, rhinestone earrings, and vintage crystals, foam cones and a bottle brush tree transform into magical miniature Jeweled Trees, *opposite*. Instructions are on page 103.

IVORY BLOOMS PILLOW Throw pillows in wintry colors and soft fabrics make it easy to adapt a home for the holiday season. Make an Ivory Blooms Pillow, *opposite*, by using shades of felt stitched to the pillow backing. Instructions are on page 102.

FOREST OF WHITE PILLOW Trees of various white prints and solid fabric overlap on a printed creamy fabric to make a Forest of White Pillow, *above*. Gold accents are added to the trees for some holiday sparkle. Instructions are on page 103.

Winter White Wreath
Shown on page 91

WHAT YOU NEED
Ivory spray paint
Purchased pinecone wreath
Reindeer figurine
Hot-glue gun and glue sticks

WHAT YOU DO
1. Be sure the wreath is clean and dry. Place it on a covered area.
2. In a well-ventilated area spray-paint the pinecone wreath. Let dry thoroughly between coats.
3. Use hot glue to adhere the reindeer to the center of the wreath. Let dry. Spray with ivory paint again. Let dry.

Centerpiece in White
Shown on page 94

WHAT YOU NEED
3 clear glass tumblers
Creamy or white items, such as
    ornaments, candies, acrylic snowflakes
White tray
White ribbon

WHAT YOU DO
Be sure the glasses are clean and dry. Fill with white or cream-color items and set on tray. Tie ribbons around the glasses.

Jewelry Brooch Package Topper
Shown on page 92

WHAT YOU NEED
Cardboard box
White cardstock
Ribbon to wrap around box and tie at top
Vintage jewelry pieces
Wire cutters (if needed)
Die-cut shape for top of box
Glitter spray, such as Glimmer Mist or
    Perfect Pearls spray

Heat gun
Hot-glue gun and glue sticks
Foam dots
Tape adhesive
Wavy trimmer or ruler

WHAT YOU DO
1. Cover box and lid with cardstock using strong tape adhesive.
2. Cut strips for edges of lid using wavy trimmer; adhere.
3. Cut die-cut piece for top of box from cardstock and spray with mist. Dry with heat gun and set aside.
4. Wrap ribbon around sides of box and tape at top.
5. Adhere the die-cut piece to top of the box using foam dots.
6. Cut two lengths of ribbon and knot together. Adhere to center of die-cut piece using hot glue. Notch ends with scissors.
7. Adhere jewelry to top of box using hot glue. (Use wire cutter if necessary to remove fasteners.)

Christmas NOEL Message
Shown on page 94

WHAT YOU NEED

Chipboard letters to spell NOEL
White acrylic paint
White or clear glitter spray, such as
    Tattered Angels Glimmer Mist
White cardstock
White crafts glue or decoupage medium
Brayer
Buttons: white, cream (new and vintage)
White and cream craft thread
Wide white or cream ribbon
Fine-tip white glue for buttons
Scissors
Self-adhesive pearls

WHAT YOU DO

1. Paint the sides of the letters with white acrylic paint. Allow to dry, then lightly spray the sides with glitter spray. Allow to dry.

2. Trace the letters onto white cardstock. Cut out. Apply glue to the chipboard. Adhere the cut-out letters, then smooth with the brayer. Allow to dry. (Use craft knife if necessary to trim excess.)

3. Tie some of the buttons with white or cream thread. Arrange buttons on the bottom portion of each letter, mixing new and vintage, white and cream. Adhere the buttons with fine-tip white glue and allow to dry.

4. Add a few pearls to the buttons, securing with additional glue if necessary. Tie ribbon to the top of the letter "O" and trim ends.

Sparkling PEACE Letters
Shown on page 93

WHAT YOU NEED

Purchased chipboard letters to spell
    PEACE or ¼-inch-thick wood to cut
    own letters
Tracing paper if using wood
Band saw if using wood
Pencil
Scissors
White acrylic paint
White or clear glitter spray, such as
    Tattered Angels Glimmer Mist
White paper: solid, white-on-white stripe,
    dotted
White crafts glue or decoupage medium
Brayer
Embossing templates (large/small dots or
    other suitable pattern)
Scissors
½" square punch
½", ¾" circle punches
Adhesive, including foam pop dots
Fine white glitter
Fine-tip white glue for glitter
Self-adhesive jewels
White craft thread

WHAT YOU DO

1. If using wood, trace patterns of large letters, *pages 100–101,* and cut out using band saw. Sand lightly. Paint the sides of the letters (chipboard or wood) with white acrylic paint. Allow to dry, then lightly spray the sides with glitter spray. Allow to dry. Trace the letters onto solid white paper. Cut out.

2. Apply glue to the wood or chipboard. Adhere the cut-out letters, then smooth with the brayer. Allow to dry. Use crafts knife if necessary to trim excess.

3. To create the winter scene detail embellishments on the letters, trace detail patterns, *pages 100–101,* and cut from patterned white papers. From striped and solid paper, cut several triangle trees and adhere to the letters using foam dots and regular adhesive. Emboss some of the trees for texture. Add jewels to other trees. Use the patterns to cut houses, then use the small square punch to make "windows" from white paper. Use the circle punches to create stylized "smoke" above the chimney. Using fine-tip adhesive, add a thin line of glitter for accents and dust with glitter. Use placement diagrams for help in placing paper accents. Allow to dry.

4. Cut two stars from white paper. Sandwich white craft thread between them, then hang from the back of the letter "C." Add a jewel to each side of the star.

**Sparkling Peace
Letters and Detail
Embellishments**

Enlarge 200%

Ivory Blooms Pillow
Shown on page 96

WHAT YOU NEED

Die-cut machine with flower dies or flower patterns, *below*
Template cutting material
Wool felt: white, natural, oatmeal
Ivory thread
¾-inch button cover kit
15-inch square ivory pillow cover

WHAT YOU DO

1. Cut the petals using a die-cut machine or, using the patterns, *below*, cut shapes from template material. Cut three sizes of petals for each poinsettia (one each in white, natural, and oatmeal). For the chrysanthemum, cut three sizes of petals from oatmeal felt. For the looped flowers, cut 3½-inch-wide and 36-inch-long strips—one 2½ inches and one 1½ inches wide.

2. To form the chrysanthemum, stack one each of the three sizes of petals, starting with the largest and ending with the smallest. With a needle and thread, sew the layers together with small stitches in the center.

3. For the poinsettia, pin a fold in each petal and sew a seam, referring to the pattern for a placement. Tie in a knot and trim threads. With the folded side down, stack one each of the three sizes of petals, starting with the largest and ending with the smallest. Sew the layers together with small stitches in the center.

4. Lay flowers on the pillow cover in a pleasing arrangement, leaving space for the looped flowers. Sew the flowers to the pillow cover with small stitches in the flower centers.

5. Following the manufacturer's directions, cover buttons with oatmeal felt. Sew a

button to the pillow cover in the center of the area where you wish to place a looped flower. Fold the looped flower strips in half lengthwise and sew the cut edges together, forming long tubes. Lay the tubes flat, with the seam flat along one side. Cut slits ¼ inch apart on the folded edges, not cutting into the stitching.

6. Starting with the 1½-inch strip, wind the end into a circle around the base of the button. Tuck the sewn edge on the inside and the loop petals on the outside. Use small stitches to hand-stitch the cut edges to the pillow cover. Encircle the button with a second row, this time enlarging the circle so the second row of looped petals extends out beyond the first.

7. Continue hand-stitching this strip in place. Leave the thread connected but cut off the remaining strip length (save it for the next flower) and switch to the

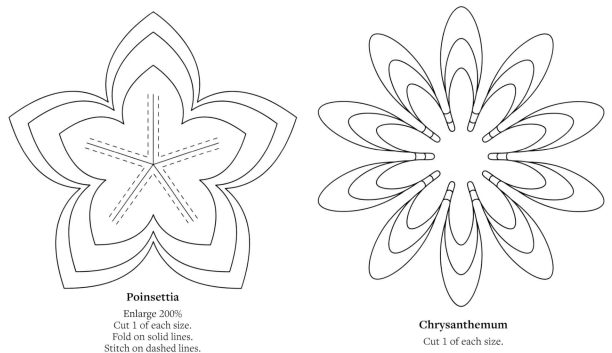

Poinsettia

Enlarge 200%
Cut 1 of each size.
Fold on solid lines.
Stitch on dashed lines.

Chrysanthemum

Cut 1 of each size.

medium-size strip. Stitch the end of the new strip where the first strip ended. Continue to enlarge the circles and stitch to the pillow. Cut off the remaining medium strip and use the large strip to make the final circle of looped petals.

Forest of White Pillow
Shown on page 97

WHAT YOU NEED
Tracing paper
½ yard ivory print fabric
Paper-backed fusible web
Fabric scraps: assorted cream and white prints
Trim, such as gold beads and cording
Gold thread; needle
14×18-inch pillow form

WHAT YOU DO
1. From ivory fabric, cut one 15×19-inch rectangle (pillow front) and two 15×12-inch rectangles (pillow back).
2. Enlarge tree and trunk patterns, *below*, onto tracing paper. Trace patterns onto paper side of fusible web, leaving one or more inches between shapes. Loosely cut round shapes. Place the fusible-web shapes, adhesive side down, on wrong sides of cream and white fabrics. Iron in place following the manufacturer's instructions. Cut out shapes along traced lines and remove paper backing.
3. Arrange tree and trunk appliques on pillow front. Using an iron on low setting, press appliques in place. Lay gold cording around each tree and couch in place. Add decorative lines and beads and sew in place.
4. For each backing piece, fold under a ½-inch hem twice along one long edge. Press and topstitch in place. Lay the backing pieces in place. Lay the backing pieces side-by-side with the hemmed edges overlapping 3 inches, creating a 15×19-inch rectangle; pin in place.
5. Place the pillow front and back with right sides together. Sew around outside edges using a ½-inch seam allowance. Trim corners, turn right side out, and press. Insert pillow form.

Jeweled Trees
Shown on page 95

For the Cone Tree

WHAT YOU NEED
Purchased foam tree shape, such as Styrofoam
Strands of pearls
Vintage crystals
Vintage jewelry
Hot-glue gun and hot-glue

WHAT YOU DO
If the jewelry has a pin back, poke it into the foam cone. Add pearls and other vintage jewelry gluing in place if necessary. Let dry. Set in silver stand.

For the Bottle Brush Tree

WHAT YOU NEED
Bottle brush tree
Bleach and water solution (1 part bleach to 4 parts water)
Plastic pail
Strands of pearls

WHAT YOU DO
Cover the surface to be worked on. In a well-ventilated area, place bleach solution in plastic pail. Carefully dip tree into solution. Let stand for 10 minutes. Check to see if tree is bleached. If so, rinse with cold water. Let dry. Wrap pearls around tree.

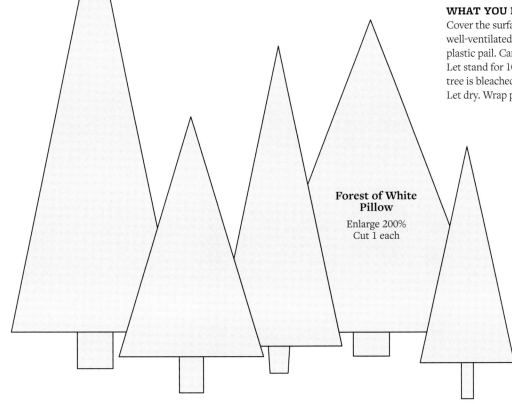

Forest of White Pillow

Enlarge 200%
Cut 1 each

'tis a gift to be simple

THE BEST GIFTS ARE HANDMADE GIFTS. This year, make gift giving simple by creating special gifts for family and friends using castaway sweaters, recycled fabrics, and bits of paper and scraps. You'll love making these easy gifts and they will love you for it!

FELTED SWEATER BAG Don't throw away that favorite sweater— make it into a stylish Felted Sweater Bag. The bag is designed to use some of the details from the sweater and has a purchased handle. Instructions are on page 116.

GIFTY SOAPS So easy to make and oh-so-lovely, Gifty Soaps, *above left,* will please friends on your holiday list. Instructions are on page 118.

EMBROIDERED GIFTY ENVELOPES The wrap is just as pretty as the gift when you make Embroidered Gifty Envelopes, *above right,* from felt scraps. A few pretty stitches make these sweet wraps heirloom quality. Instructions begin on page 122.

CHENILLE DIAPER BAG AND CHANGING PAD Soft and sweet, this Chenille Diaper Bag, *opposite,* will be a welcome gift for the new mom and dad. Use matching fabric to make a handy Changing Pad. Instructions are on page 119.

DESIGNER EYEGLASS CASES For those special people on your list, create Designer Eyeglass Cases, *above left*, using favorite fabrics and a few embroidery stitches. Instructions are on page 118.

YO-YO SACHET Several tiny yo-yos stitched in rich, shiny fabrics combine to make a sweet Yo-Yo Sachet, *above right*—the perfect gift. Use a needle and thread to take little stitches and sew the yo-yos in a row forming a square on top of the pillow. Instructions are on page 120.

SO-SIMPLE HAT AND MITTEN SET Knit a So-Simple Easy Hat and Mitten Set, *above*, just in time for cold weather. The set is so easy to make you can make one in the nick of time for that last-minute gift—and in the color that suits that special person. The set is worked in simple stockinette stitch and topped with a tassel. Instructions begin on page 124.

DOGGY CHEW TOYS Don't forget little Rex this year when you are giving gifts! Make him some Doggy Chew Toys, *above right*, that he will love to carry around on Christmas morning. Instructions are on page 119.

MUSIC PICTURE FRAME Celebrate the musical folks on your Christmas list with a personalized Music Picture Frame, *above left*. The embellishments are just rolled-up pieces of sheet music. Instructions are on page 118.

WOOL PLAID WINTER SET Be the creator of a one-of-a-kind designer-style Wool Plaid Winter Set, *opposite*. The set is made using discarded sweaters that have been felted and then pieced together using elements from the original sweater. Felt flowers adorn the hat and scarf. Instructions are on page 120.

QUILTED POT HOLDERS A favorite quilt block pattern is made into Quilted Pot holders, *opposite*, that will be enjoyed during holiday baking time. Choose your own block pattern or use the Tree of Life pattern we have chosen. Instructions are on page 125.

CHRISTMAS-COLOR CHARM BRACELET String up a few bracelets this year for those special people on your list. The Christmas-Color Charm Bracelet, *above left*, is extra special because it uses two strands of beads as the main part of the bracelet. Instructions are on page 117.

VINTAGE FRAME TRIO Preserve favorite vintage fabrics by copying them and showcasing the prints in a Vintage Frame Trio, *above right*. The striking patterns become colorful art. Instructions are on page 120.

"MAKING A LIST" GREETING CARD Santa is the star on this clever card, which features a purchased chipboard sticker.

CHRISTMAS LIGHTS CARD Paper Christmas lights are strung together with colorful twine for a clever holiday greeting.

SNOWMAN CARD Warm wishes are easy to send when you make a snowman card from scraps of paper.

HAPPY HOLIDAYS GREETING A single paper ornament is the 3-dimensional appeal of this sweet card.

CHRISTMAS TREE CARD Let die-cuts and stickers help you create cards by the dozens this year. Instructions for all of the cards begin on page 126.

Felted Sweater Bag

Shown on page 105

WHAT YOU NEED

Tracing paper or copier

Preshrunk wool sweater with pocket (see felting tips, *right*)

Purchased purse handles (6½ inches wide×4¾ inches high)

Scrap from plain shirt flannel or ⅓ yard of flannel fabric to match sweater color

⅓ yard medium-weight iron-on interfacing

Matching thread

Pins; scissors

One 1-inch coat button

Buttonhole thread

WHAT YOU DO

1. Enlarge and trace or copy patterns, *below* and *opposite*. Cut purse pattern from bottom of sweater fabric, having top straight edge of pattern aligned along bottom ribbing edge, with the ribbing extending beyond the straight edge of the pattern. Cut one purse pattern from the front of the sweater and one from the back of the sweater.

2. Slit open the sleeves of the sweater, iron the piece flat, and cut two outside pocket pieces with the straight top edge of the pocket at the edge of the sleeve ribbing. Trim the neckline ribbing from the sweater to be used as the loop closure. Cut lining pieces from a recycled flannel shirt or other flannel fabric. Cut two purse body pieces from iron-on interfacing, cutting interfacing even with top fold line marked on pattern.

3. Iron interfacing to the back of the flannel lining pieces. For the lining pockets, iron ½-inch seam to the back of side and bottom edges; clip curved edges. Fold and iron top edge of lining pocket ¼ inch and another ½ inch under. Topstitch pocket top along folded edge to hem. Place wrong side of lining pocket to right side of lining purse pieces, placing in center of purse, 2 inches down from top fold line. Stitch pockets close to folded side and bottom edges, reinforcing at tip corners.

4. With right sides together, stitch purse lining pieces together at side and bottom edges, starting at point indicated on pattern. Clip curves. Narrowly hem remaining open side edges. Sew sweater pockets to front sweater fabric, placing at center and 1¾ inches from bottom edge. Stitch close to cut edges, reinforcing at top corners. (There is no need to fold under raw edges since the felted wool doesn't ravel.) With right sides together, stitch a ¼-inch seam on the side and lower edges of purse, starting and stopping at points indicated by an X on the pattern.

5. Make a depth tuck or dart in both lining and sweater fabrics as indicated on the pattern forming the darts with right sides together. Trim sweater seams to ¼ inch. Do not trim lining seams. Flip the lining darts up.

6. Make loop closure from 7-inch ribbing taken from neckline of sweater. With wrong sides in, fold length together to make strip about ¾ inch wide. Fold strip in half and insert between lining and purse at center of one side at the top, cut ends extending down onto the seam allowance. Insert lining into purse, with wrong sides together. Pin top and side edges, placing fold of lining at purse fold line. Sew lining to purse, stitching close to side edges and across fold line.

7. Insert handles by folding top ribbing edge through handles and lapping over to purse front. Pin through both layers, forming a casing for handles. Stitch through all layers, just above ribbing edge, gathering purse together to slide along handles as you sew across the bag. Sew large coat button to the side opposite the loop closure, using buttonhole thread to secure button. Trim ribbing at side edges, fold seam under and hand-stitch the ribbing together at side edges.

TIPS FOR FELTING WOOL SWEATERS

1. Choose sweaters with 100% wool fiber content or as much wool as possible for best shrinkage. Sweaters containing angora rabbit hair also shrink and felt well.

2. Wash sweaters in very hot water with a small amount of laundry soap. Agitation of the washing machine helps to loosen the fibers and shrink the wool. Placing sweaters inside old pillowcases during the wash will save your washing machine and drains from clogging up with the thousands of tiny fibers that wash out of the sweaters.

3. Dry sweaters in very hot dryer to shrink and felt the item the maximum amount.

4. To keep from stretching the fabric out of shape when sewing by machine, try using an even-feed or walking foot attachment. It is also helpful to lengthen the stitch slightly and lighten the pressure placed on the presser foot of the sewing machine.

5. Tightly felted wool does not ravel, and edges and seams can usually be left raw or unfinished similar to regular felt.

**Felted Sweater Bag
Inside Sweater Pocket**

Enlarge 225%
Cut 2 from felted sweater

**Felted Sweater Bag
Outside Lining**

Enlarge 225%
Cut 2 from lining

6. If wool fabric shrinks up so dense and thick that it is hard to sew by machine, hand-stitch pieces together. Use pretty yarns for a special decorative effect. Even thick, dense wool is fairly easy to pull yarn through.

7. When choosing sweaters to recycle and determining projects to make, look closely at the individual design elements of the original sweater for inspiration in making projects. For example, button-front openings add nice details for edgings on scarves or flaps of purses. And save every button for trim details on mittens or purses. Wide bottom ribbing edges are great for hat bottoms. Wide ribbing neck edges of sweaters could provide openings for a drawstring purse. Ribbed edges of sleeves are perfect for mitten cuffs.

8. Use your imagination, letting the colors, designs, and details from the original sweater determine the overall look of your felted project.

Christmas-Color Charm Bracelet
Shown on page 113

WHAT YOU NEED
Clear fine beading elastic thread
Green pearlized beads
Strong glue, such as Super Glue
Glass beads in green and red
Silver beads
Nickel-size circular "O" bead with 2 holes
Three 1-inch-long jewelry pins
Round-nose pliers

WHAT YOU DO
1. String two lengths of elastic thread with green pearlized beads to fit wrist. Knot ends of each length securely; dot knots with glue. Thread jewelry pins with desired beads, using the photo for inspiration.

2. To make charms, form the straight end of each pin into a circle using round-nose pliers. Secure the center pin around both bracelet strands to connect them together. Secure the remaining two pins to one of the two bracelets, one on each side of the center charm.

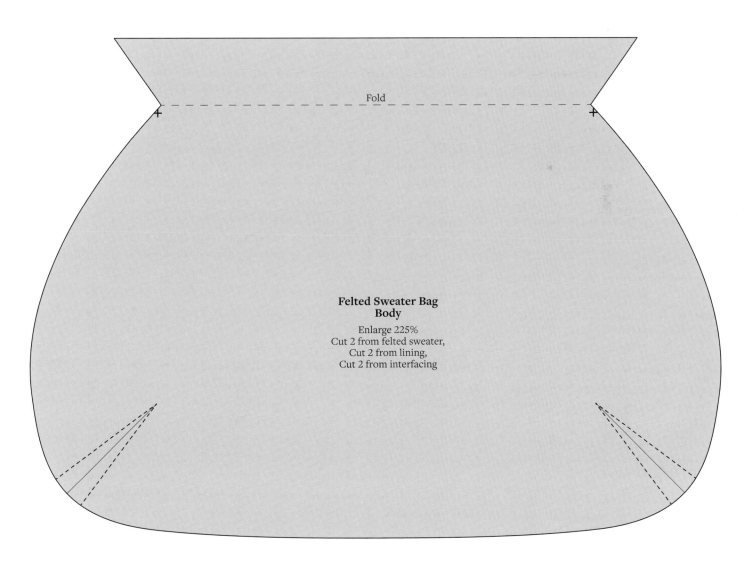

Felted Sweater Bag Body

Enlarge 225%
Cut 2 from felted sweater,
Cut 2 from lining,
Cut 2 from interfacing

Fold

Gifty Soaps
Shown on page 106

WHAT YOU NEED

Purchased Christmas soap
Scrapbook paper
Scissor; crafts glue
Sticker

WHAT YOU DO

Measure around the soap and cut a piece of paper about ½ inch wide and long enough to wrap around the soap. Glue the strip around the soap. Add a sticker.

Designer Eyeglass Cases
Shown on page 108

WHAT YOU NEED

Tracing paper
Pencil
8×8-inch square suedelike fabric
8×8-inch square flannel fabric for lining
8×8-inch square medium-weight iron-on
    interfacing
Decorative threads, embroidery floss,
    or perle cotton
Matching sewing threads

WHAT YOU DO

1. Trace pattern, *right*, onto tracing paper and cut out. Cut one pattern from the suedelike fabric, flip the pattern, and cut one from flannel and interfacing. Fuse interfacing to back side of suedelike fabric. Couch on decorative threads onto right side of case outside fabric.

2. With right sides together, stitch lining to outside case along the top curved edge, using ½-inch seam allowance. Grade seam allowance and press toward the lining. With right sides of case and lining together, stitch along longest side from the top seam line down the long side for 1 inch using ½-inch seam allowance. Trim seam; clip corners.

3. Match lining to lining fabric and outside to outside fabric, with right sides together. Stitch around the entire edge, using ½-inch seam allowance, leaving an opening along the lining seam line to allow for turning. Stop at the top seam line, flip the seam allowance that was previously sewn and trimmed, and continue sewing from the seam allowance down the side and around the bottom edge. Trim the seam allowance and clip corners. Turn right side out and stitch opening closed. Push the lining into the outside case fabric and press. (**Note:** A chopstick is helpful in poking the lining into the corners inside the case.)

Music Picture Frame
Shown on page 110

WHAT YOU NEED

Purchased flat-front picture frame
Old sheet music
Scissors
Crafts glue

WHAT YOU DO

1. Cut the music into 1×2-inch pieces. Make at least 50 to 100 pieces. Starting from the long end of each piece, roll up tightly and glue to secure.

2. Glue the pieces side by side around the edge of the frame. Allow to dry.

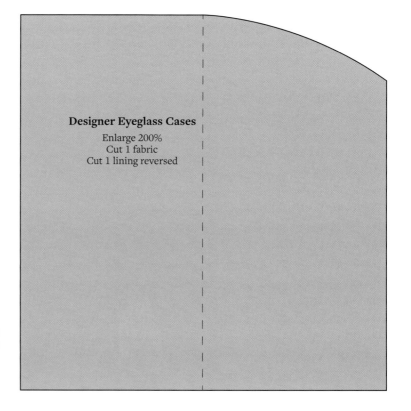

Designer Eyeglass Cases
Enlarge 200%
Cut 1 fabric
Cut 1 lining reversed

Chenille Diaper Bag and Changing Pad

Shown on page 107

WHAT YOU NEED

Two 16½×19½-inch pieces chenille for bag body

Two 3½×32-inch pieces chenille for handles

Two 16½×19½-inch pieces heavy-weight sew-in interfacing

Four 6½×8-inch pieces cotton fabric for pockets

One 1¼×32-inch strip cotton fabric for top decorative trim

One 2½×8½-inch piece cotton fabric for tab closing

One 2½×8½-inch piece medium-weight iron-on interfacing for tab

One 2½×8½-inch piece thin cotton batting for tab

One ¾-inch snap for tab closing

Two 6×7½-inch pieces medium-weight iron-on interfacing for pockets

One 9×6-inch piece heavy cardboard for reinforced bottom

One 9×12-inch piece thin cotton batting to cover cardboard

One 9½×12½-inch piece cotton fabric to cover cardboard

Two 15×21½-inch pieces cotton fabric for changing pad

One 15×21½-inch piece thin cotton batting for changing pad

Assorted decorative buttons

Matching sewing thread

WHAT YOU DO

1. Layer 16×19½-inch pieces of interfacing on back of bag chenille pieces and baste all around. With right sides together, stitch front to back, around side and lower edges, in ½-inch seam, overcasting edges. Turn top edge under ½ inch to the inside of the bag and stitch. Turn again 2 inches to the inside. On the inside of the bag, with right sides together, line up seam lines to make a triangle inside at corners. Mark a line perpendicular to the seam line, 2 inches from the point. Stitch across the drawn line, through both front and back, to add depth to the bag. Trim seam to ½ inch and overcast edges.

2. With right sides together, stitch long seam of each handle in ½-inch seam. Fold ½ inch to inside at each end. Turn and press. Place handles 4 inches from side seams, extending down on the inside 1½ inches. Stitch across handles through bag front and back, at topstitching, down sides, and along bottom end of handle, forming a square to reinforce handles.

3. Sew buttons to chenille to embellish. Iron interfacing to the back of two pocket pieces. With right sides together, stitch pocket lining pieces to interfaced pockets, stitching around side and lower edges using ¼-inch seam. Clip corners, turn, and press. Press ¼ inch in along top edge of the pocket and edge stitch. Pin pockets to sides of tote. Stitch around side and lower edges through bag.

4. For decorative tape at top edge of bag, press in ¼ inch along both long side edges of fabric strip (bias tape maker tool is helpful for this). Stitch tape to top edge of bag, stitching close to both pressed edges of tape. Make tab closure by ironing interfacing to back of 2½×8½-inch piece of fabric. Layer batting on back of fabric strip and fold in half with right sides of fabric short ends together. Stitch down long side edges in ¼-inch seam. Turn, fold bottom edges in ¼ inch, and press. Place tab with open end inside back top edge of bag at the center. Stitch along previous stitching lines for the binding to attach tab to bag. Sew decorative buttons to the end of the tab. Sew snap under the tab below buttons and to bag top edge.

5. Wrap 9½×12½-inch piece of fabric around batting, folding in ¼-inch seams. Stitch around outside edges to encase batting-wrapped cardboard.

6. Make changing mat by layering fabrics right sides together. Place batting on back side of one piece of fabric. Stitch around outside edges using ¼-inch seam and leaving an opening for turning. Clip corners, turn, and press. Edge stitch around outside edges of mat and quilt as desired.

Doggy Chew Toys

Shown on page 110

WHAT YOU NEED

FOR THE BRAIDED TOY

¼ yard each of red and white felt

Masking tape

Scissors

Red twine

FOR THE BALL TOY

12×10-inch piece of felt

Scissors

Tennis ball

Red twine

WHAT YOU DO

1. For the Braided Toy, cut the felt into 2×12-inch pieces. Lay three pieces together at the top and tape to a table. Braid the felt. Tie the ends with red twine or small strips of felt.

2. For the Ball Toy, lay the felt on a table. Lay the ball in the middle of the felt. Wrap around the ball and tie with twine.

Depending on size and age of dog, watch dog to prevent choking when given a new toy.

Wool Plaid Winter Set
Shown on page 111

WHAT YOU NEED FOR ALL PIECES
Tracing paper
Castaway 100% wool sweaters that have
   been felted (See page 159 for felting
   instructions)
Matching thread
Scissors
Felt colors to coordinate with sweater
   (for flowers)
Buttons (for flowers)

For the Scarf
WHAT YOU DO

1. Using scraps from felted sweaters, cut
blocks of varying lengths and 5-inch
widths. Include scraps of coordinating
felted wool. End pieces are cut from the
front button opening. Bottom edges are
scraps of the collar ribbing from sweater
neck edge.

2. Align cut edges together and stitch with
zigzag machine stitch so that stitching
sews over each piece to join fabric
together. Add sections until scarf is
54 inches or desired length.

For the Hat
WHAT YOU DO

1. Enlarge and trace pattern, *opposite*, and
cut two hat patterns from bottom edge of
sweater, aligning long straight edge with
bottom edge of ribbing. Make tiny darts as
indicated by dotted lines on the pattern.
With right sides together, sew around hat,
leaving bottom open. Turn right side out.

2. Embellish side front with flower made
from pattern cut from scraps of sweater,
wool felt, or felt and button sewn in the
center. (**Note:** Use button from original
sweater if desired.) Wear hat with ribbing
band down or folded up.

For the Mittens
WHAT YOU DO

1. Enlarge and trace patterns, *opposite*, and
cut out. Lay straight side of pattern on
finished edge of sweater. Cut two pieces
for each mitten.

2. With right sides together, sew around
edge of mitten shape using a ¼-inch seam.
Turn and press. Add flower decorations
if desired.

For the Flowers
WHAT YOU DO

1. Enlarge and trace flower and leaf
patterns, *opposite*, onto tracing paper. Draw
around pattern on desired color of felt.
Cut out.

2. Layer felt flowers as desired. Place leaf
shapes behind flowers. Use small stitches
to sew pieces together. Add button in the
middle. Sew to wool piece as desired.

Vintage Frame Trio
Shown on page 113

WHAT YOU NEED
3 small gold picture frames
Lightweight cardboard
Vintage fabric, such as a tablecloth
Copier
Scissors
Small buttons
Crafts glue

WHAT YOU DO

1. Measure the inside of the frames. Cut
cardboard piece to fit the measurement.
Photocopy the vintage fabric.

2. Lay cardboard piece on fabric and cut
three pieces to fit inside the frames. Place
inside the frames and secure in place. Glue
buttons to the edges of the frames.

Yo-Yo Sachet
Shown on page 108

WHAT YOU NEED
Small pieces of fabric for yo-yos
Matching thread
Needle
Scissors
Small purchased pillow sachet
Cording

WHAT YOU DO

1. Cut fabric circles to make the desired
size yo-yo to fit the pillow. The circle will
become quite a bit smaller when you make
it into a yo-yo. The diameter of the finished
circle will be half the size of the circle of
fabric you start with. For example, for a
1-inch finished yo-yo, you will need a
2-inch circle. Draw around the circle onto
the fabric that you have chosen. Cut out
the circle.

2. Thread the needle. Tie a knot at the end
of the thread. Turn under a scant ¼ inch of
fabric as you work running stitches close to
the folded edge. Don't make the stitches
too tiny or the hole of the yo-yo will be too
big. Make the stitches about ¼ inch apart.

3. Continue to sew all around the circle
until you have come back to where you
started sewing. The yo-yo will flatten out a
bit and curl up on the edges. Bring the
needle out to the side without the cut edge.

4. Pull the needle firmly to gather up the
stitches and draw the yo-yo closed. The
yo-yo will bunch up and become 3-D. Take
a few more little stitches where the thread
comes out to hold the yo-yo in place.
Adjust the gathers in the yo-yo and flatten
it down. Add any embellishments you like,
such as a button, pin, or another small
yo-yo on top.

5. Sew the yo-yos to the top of the pillow.
Tack the ends of the cording to the corners
of the pillow.

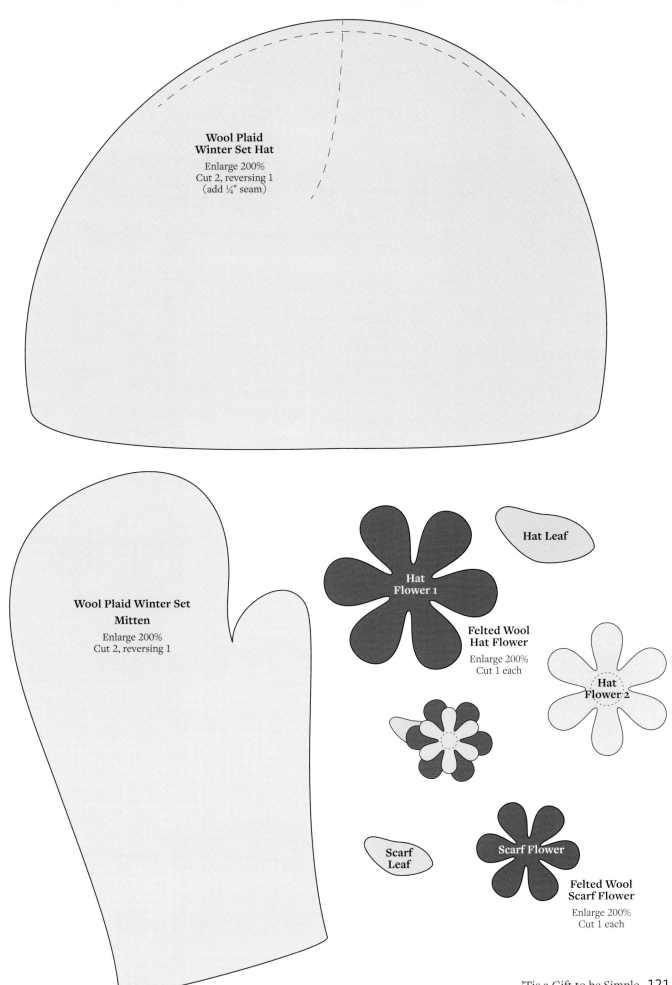

**Wool Plaid
Winter Set Hat**

Enlarge 200%
Cut 2, reversing 1
(add ¼" seam)

**Wool Plaid Winter Set
Mitten**

Enlarge 200%
Cut 2, reversing 1

Hat Leaf

Hat
Flower 1

**Felted Wool
Hat Flower**

Enlarge 200%
Cut 1 each

Hat
Flower 2

Scarf
Leaf

Scarf Flower

**Felted Wool
Scarf Flower**

Enlarge 200%
Cut 1 each

Embroidered Gifty Envelopes

Shown on page 106

WHAT YOU NEED

One 9½×12-inch piece of wool felt for each envelope

6 strand embroidery floss: DMC yellow 743, green 703, and red 304

One button for each envelope in red or green colors

Embroidery needle

Pins

Water-soluble marking pen

WHAT YOU DO

1. Enlarge and trace pattern, *opposite*, and cut out. Lay on the felt. Fold on lines indicated.

2. Embroider the envelopes (see "Embroidering"). After embroidering is finished, measure the button for a buttonhole. Determine the placement for the button and cut a horizontal slit in the flap. Sew the button to the felt under the slit, aligning the button making sure not to sew through the bottom layer of the envelope.

EMBROIDERING

1. Transfer the patterns, *opposite,* onto the felt with transfer pen. Separate the strands of embroidery floss and divide. Use 2 strands for the embroidering.

For the Yellow Envelope

WHAT YOU DO

1. Embroider the flower using the Lazy Daisy Stitch and red floss. Embroider the vine with the Stem Stitch and green floss. Stitch the leaves with the Lazy Daisy Stitch and green floss.

2. Stitch a smaller flower and leaves in each side corner, one inch from each side edge. Stitch 3 Lazy Daisy Stitches with red floss and 2 Lazy Daisy Stitches with green floss. Add 2 French Knots with green floss.

3. Fold the bottom section up again at the fold line and pin side edges. Stitch the side edges together with a Blanket Stitch and red floss. Sew the diagonal edges of the top flap with the Buttonhole Stitch and red floss.

4. Align a red button to be centered under the flower, cut buttonhole, and sew button.

For the Red Envelope

WHAT YOU DO

1. With the yellow floss, sew a flower centered above the point with double Lazy Daisy Stitches. Sew a French Knot at the center with green floss. Sew Lazy Daisy Stitches along the diagonal edge with green floss and the French Knots with yellow floss. Sew Lazy Daisy Stitches at the bottom on each side edge with green floss and French Knots with yellow floss.

2. Fold the bottom section up again at the fold line and pin side edges. Stitch the side edges together with a Running Stitch and yellow floss.

3. Align a green button to be centered above the yellow flower, cut buttonhole, and sew button.

For the White Envelope

WHAT YOU DO

1. With red floss, sew Lazy Daisy flowers along the diagonal edges of the flap. Sew

French Knot

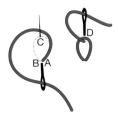

Lazy Daisy

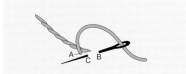

Blanket Stich

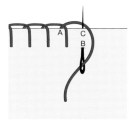

Stem Stitch

Running Stitch

Embroidered Gift Envelope **Green Envelope** Placement Diagram

Embroidered Gift Envelope **White Envelope** Placement Diagram

Embroidered Gift Envelope **Red Envelope** Placement Diagram

Embroidered Gift Envelope **Yellow Envelope** Placement Diagram

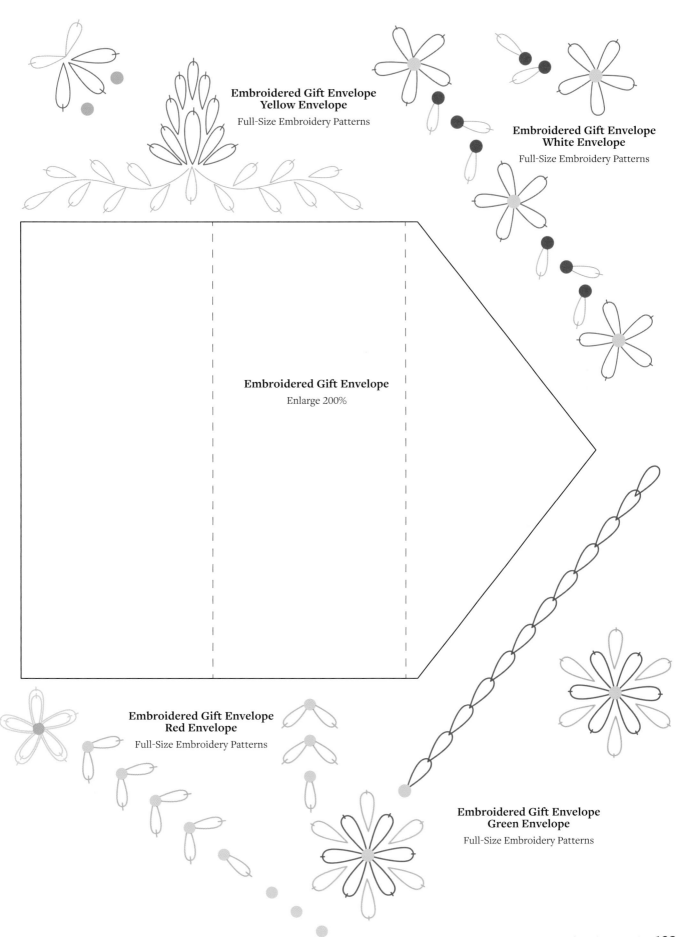

Embroidered Gift Envelope
Yellow Envelope
Full-Size Embroidery Patterns

Embroidered Gift Envelope
White Envelope
Full-Size Embroidery Patterns

Embroidered Gift Envelope
Enlarge 200%

Embroidered Gift Envelope
Red Envelope
Full-Size Embroidery Patterns

Embroidered Gift Envelope
Green Envelope
Full-Size Embroidery Patterns

the Lazy Daisy Stitches with green floss and the French knots with red floss.

2. Sew a red Lazy Daisy flower on each bottom edge 1 inch from the side edges.

3. Fold the bottom section up again at the fold line and pin side edges. Stitch the side edges together with a Running Stitch and green floss.

4. Align a red button to be centered above the flowers at the point, cut buttonhole, and sew button.

For the Green Envelope
WHAT YOU DO

1. Sew a Lazy Daisy flower centered at the point on the flap with red floss and the leaves with green floss. Sew the French Knots with yellow floss. Sew a straight line Chain Stitch ½ inch from the diagonal edges of the flap with red floss.

2. Sew the Lazy Daisy flower and leaves on each side edge of the bottom flap, ¾ inch from the side and bottom edges.

3. Fold the bottom section up again at the fold line and pin side edges. Stitch the side edges together with a Running Stitch and red floss.

4. Align a red button to be centered above the flower, cut buttonhole, and sew button.

So-Simple Mittens
Shown on page 109

Skill Level: Easy
Size: Small (M, L)
Width: 4 (4½, 5)"
Length: 9½ (10¼, 11)"

WHAT YOU NEED
Patons Shetland Chunky, 75% acrylic/25% wool, bulky-weight yard (148 yards per ball): For all sizes, 1 ball of Plum Crazy (3728)
Size 6 (4 mm) knitting needles or size needed to obtain gauge

Yarn needle
Two ring-type stitch markers

GAUGE
In St st (knit RS rows, purl WS rows), 15 sts and 24 rows = 4"/10 cm. **TAKE TIME TO CHECK YOUR GAUGE.**

SPECIAL ABBREVIATIONS
M1: Lift running thread before next stitch onto left-hand needle and knit in its back loop to make one stitch.

Ssk: Slip next 2 sts knitwise, one at a time to right-hand needle; insert tip of left-hand needle into fronts of these 2 sts and k tog.

Pm: Place a marker.

WHAT YOU DO
Cast on 25 (29, 33) sts. Beg with a purl row, work 5 St st rows. Inc 1 st each edge now and then every 4th row twice more—31 (35, 39) sts. Work even to approx 2½ (3, 3½)" from beg, ending with a WS row.

THUMB
Row 1 (RS): K15 (17, 19) sts, pm, M1, k1, M1, pm, k15 (17, 19).
Row 2: Purl.
Row 3: K to marker, sl marker, M1, k to marker, M1, sl marker, k to end of row. Rep Rows 2-3 until there are 13 (13, 15) sts between markers. Purl next row, removing markers.
Next Row: K across, placing thumb sts onto a spare strand of yarn. Work even on the 30 (34, 38) sts until piece measures approx 8½ (9, 9½)" from beg, ending with a WS row and pm after 15th (17th, 19th) st.

TOP SHAPING
Dec Row (RS): Ssk, k to 2 sts before marker, k2tog, sl marker, ssk, k to last 2 sts, k2tog. Next Row: Pul. Rep last 2 rows until 18 (18, 22) sts rem. On next RS row, (k2tog) across. P9 (9, 10). Leaving a long tail for sewing, cut yarn.

CLOSURE
Thread tail into yarn needle. Beg with the last st on needle, take yarn back through rem sts, twice. Pull up to tightly close opening. Join sides tog.

THUMB
With RS facing, return sts to needle. Join yarn and k13 (13, 15). Next Row: P5 (5, 7), p2tog, p6. Work 6 (6, 8) more St st rows on the 12 (12, 14) sts. Next Row: (K2tog) across. Cut yarn, leaving a 10" tail. Rep Closure as for Top. Join thumb seam. Darn opening. Weave in loose ends on WS of fabric.

SECOND MITTEN
Work as for first mitten.

So-Simple Hat
Shown on page 109

Skill Level: Easy
Size: To fit an average adult
Width: 4 (4½, 5)"
Length: 19" around

WHAT YOU NEED
Patons, Shetland Chunky, 75% acrylic/15% wool, chunky-weight yarn (148 yards per skein); 1 skein of Plum Crazy (03728)
Size 10 (6 mm) knitting needles or size needed to obtain gauge
Yarn needle

GAUGE
In St st (knit RS rows, purl WS rows, 15 sts and 20 rows = 4"/10 cm. **TAKE TIME TO CHECK YOUR GAUGE.**

SPECIAL ABBREVIATIONS
M1: Lift running thread before next stitch onto left-hand needle and knit in its back loop to make one stitch.

NOTE
Add a pom-pom to top of cap if desired.

WHAT YOU DO
1. Cast on 67 sts. Work 4 rows.

2. Garter St (knit every row) noting first row is WS.

3. Next Row (WS): (K13, M1) 4 times, k15—71 sts.

4. Beg with a knit row, work in St st until Cap measures approx 4¾" from beg, ending with a purl row.

TOP SHAPING
Row 1 (RS): K1; * k2tog, k8; rep from * to end of row—64 sts.
Row 2 and all WS rows: Purl.
Row 3: K1; * k2tog, k7; rep from * to end of row—57 sts.
Row 5: K1; * k2tog, k6; rep from * to end

of row—50 sts. Cont in this manner, dec 7 sts evenly across RS rows until there are 8 sts. Break yarn, leaving a long end. Draw end through rem sts and fasten securely. Sew center back seam. Weave in ends.

Quilted Potholders
Shown on page 112

Note: You can choose any quilt block pattern you like to make these potholders. The pot holders are based on a 9-inch quilt block.

WHAT YOU NEED
⅓ yard each of 2 colors of fabric or 1 fat quarter each of 2 colors of fabric
Scrap of brown fabric for trunk
Matching sewing threads
11-inch square of heat-protective batting
11-inch square of cotton fabric for backing
50-inch length of 2½-inch strip of cotton fabric for binding
Matching sewing thread
Scissors

For the Tree of Life Block
WHAT YOU DO
1. Enlarge pattern, *right*, onto tracing paper or make templates adding ¼-inch seam allowance on all pieces. Cut pieces in desired colors. (**Note:** The Tree of Life Quilt is an early quilt pattern that was often made using two basic colors.)

2. Referring to the pattern, *right*, make DD unit (28 times).

3. Sew G to H, and G to Hr; add each unit to F. Join FGH with E pieces to complete trunk section.

4. Assemble DD units with C, A, and B pieces to make the 3 top rows and join the rows into top section.

5. Make left section in 4 vertical rows and join the rows. For right section, add a row of DD units to trunk section.

6. Join the left and right sections, then add to top section to complete the block.

To make the Pot holders
WHAT YOU DO
1. Layer quilt square, heat protective batting, and backing. Quilt around design as desired.

2. Prepare binding and sew around outside edge of square, starting at top corner, mitering corners, and ending with loop at top corner.

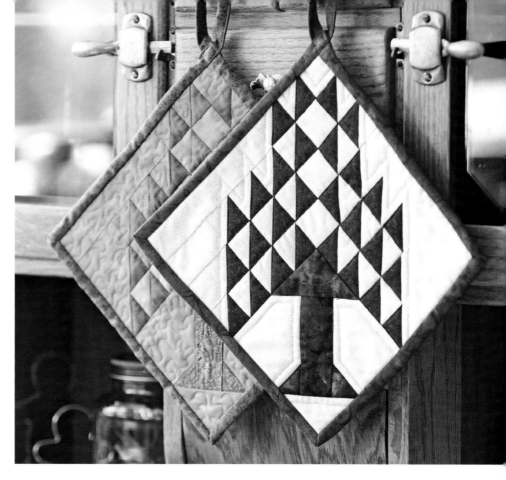

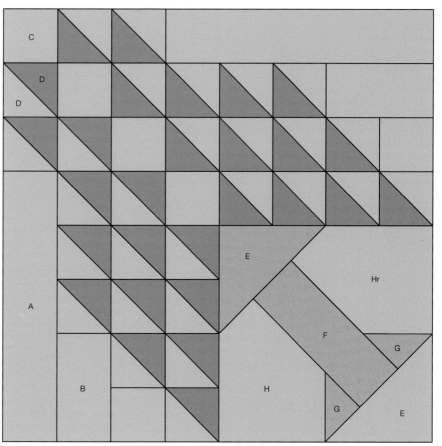

Tree of Life Quilted Pot Holder
Enlarge 200%

"Making a List" Greeting Card

Shown on page 114

WHAT YOU NEED

5½×8½-inch piece of maroon cardstock
3½×5-inch piece of teal cardstock
1-inch maroon punched circle
"Making a List" text piece (Echo Park Season's Greetings Line) or similar piece
Chipboard Santa and Believe word
2 strips of coordinating paper ½×6-inch and 1×6-inch
Red/cream bakers' twine
3½×5-inch piece of cream cardstock printed or stamped with inside greeting
Scoring blade for folding card
Trimmer
Adhesive, including adhesive dots and fine-tip liquid glue
Scissors
Ink for aging edges of pieces

WHAT YOU DO

1. Score and fold maroon card base in half (completed card measures 4¼×5½). Ink edges. Card opens at bottom. Ink and adhere teal cardstock to front center of card.

2. Use scissors to notch the end of the 1×6-inch border strip; ink and adhere across lower portion of card, flush with right edge. Trim. Leave notched end loose and bend upward. Cut the ½×6-inch paper strip at an angle; ink and adhere across lower portion of card and flush with right edge, slightly overlapping previous strip. Trim. Leave cut end loose and bend upward.

3. Ink "Making a List." Wrap twine twice around card and tie in a bow at left, then adhere the card with dimensional dots to right portion of card. Secure the twine bow with a tiny dot of liquid glue. Allow to dry.

4. Adhere the Santa to lower right corner of "Making a List," slightly off edge. Ink and

adhere burgundy circle to upper left portion of card. Adhere "Believe" to circle. Cut out, ink, and adhere greeting to inside of card.

Happy Holidays Greeting

Shown on page 115

WHAT YOU NEED

5½×8½-inch piece of maroon cardstock
½×4¼-inch piece of cream cardstock for text strip, printed or stamped with "Happy Holidays"
2×4¼-inch piece of coordinating paper
Chipboard ornament
Red/cream bakers' twine
3½×5-inch piece of cream cardstock, printed or stamped with inside greeting
Scoring blade for folding card
Trimmer; scissors
Corner rounder
Adhesive
Ink for aging edges of pieces

WHAT YOU DO

1. Score and fold maroon card base in half (completed card measures 4¼×5½). Card opens at right. Round upper left and lower right corners, then ink card base. Ink the 2×4¼-inch paper and adhere to the top portion of the card. Leave the top edge free of adhesive so that the twine can be tucked under it.

2. Insert a short length of twine into the hole in the chipboard ornament and adhere it to the back side. Adhere the ornament to the lower portion of the card. Extend the other end of the twine across the patterned paper strip and tuck the end under the top edge.

3. Tie a second piece of twine in a bow around the other piece, positioned at the top of the ornament. Cut out the text strip and adhere just below the patterned paper (slip it under the twine). Trim ends.

4. Cut out, ink, and adhere greeting to inside of card.

Snowman Card

Shown on page 115

WHAT YOU NEED

Tracing paper
5½×8½-inch piece of white cardstock
4×5¼-inch piece of mat cut from teal snowflake paper
¼×4¼-inch strip of coordinating striped patterned paper
Additional coordinating paper for snowman
Additional white cardstock for snowman, snow, and inside greeting
Green and brown cardstock for tree
Black cardstock for face
Scoring blade for folding card
Trimmer
Adhesive, including fine-tip liquid glue and pop dots
Embossing folder
⅝-inch circle punch

Snowman Card
Full-Size Pattern

Small hole punches
Scissors; pencil
Tree punch
Snowflake punch
Printer or stamps for outside and inside
	greeting

WHAT YOU DO

1. Score and fold white card base in half (completed card measures 4¼×5½ inches). Card opens at right.

2. Draw a curve along the middle front of card for snow. Cut along curve, removing the top portion of the card.

3. Cut two additional curvy strips of white cardstock, each 4¼ inches wide. Emboss one of the strips, then layer them on the front of the card, using pop dots under the top strip for dimension. Adhere a strip of striped paper across the bottom of the card. Cut and adhere the snow paper to the inside of the card. Print outside greeting and cut to fit front of card.

4. For tree, punch three trees from green cardstock. Leave one punched piece intact, then cut off the other two punched pieces to create shorter layers. Cut "fringe" along the bottom of each piece, then adhere together. Punch a trunk from brown cardstock and adhere to the tree, then adhere the tree to the snow on right portion of the card.

5. For snowman, trace the snowman pattern, *opposite,* onto white cardstock and cut out. From coordinating paper, cut a scarf (for front and back) and a triangle nose. Punch buttons and eyes, then cut a mouth from black cardstock. For hat, punch two ⅝-inch circles from coordinating paper and adhere back to back. Cut off the bottom portion to create a hat, then adhere to the snowman's head. Add a strip of coordinating paper and a punched dot as trim. Adhere snowman to left portion of card using dimensional dots.

6. Punch and adhere 2 or 3 snowflakes to the teal background. Print inside greeting; cut to fit inside the card, below the snow.

Christmas Tree Card
Shown on page 115

WHAT YOU NEED

5½×8½-inch piece green cardstock base
4×5¼-inch piece cream cardstock mat
2×4¼-inch piece coordinating patterned
	paper
Christmas Trees die cut or desired die cut
Border strip punched from green
	cardstock/backed with red
Punched or die-cut Christmas tree made
	from green cardstock
Teal punched dots or jewels for
	"ornaments"

Small chipboard or punched star
Natural twine
3½×5-inch cream cardstock, printed or
	stamped with inside greeting
Scoring blade for folding card
Trimmer
Adhesive, including fine-tip liquid glue and
	adhesive dots
Border punch
Small hole punch
Scissors
Ink for aging edges of pieces

WHAT YOU DO

1. Score and fold green card base in half (completed card measures 4¼×5½ inches). Card opens at right.

2. Ink card base. Ink and adhere cream cardstock mat to front of card. Ink and adhere patterned paper strip to lower front of card. Punch and adhere border strip across top edge of patterned paper.

3. Adhere "Christmas Trees" with dimensional dots flush with right side of card and extending above paper strip. Ink and adhere tree above text.

4. Punch and adhere "ornaments" to tree. Adhere star to top of tree. Tie twine in small bow and adhere under star with a tiny dot of liquid glue. Allow to dry.

5. Cut out, ink, and adhere greeting to inside of card.

Christmas Lights Card
Shown on page 114

WHAT YOU NEED

5½×8½-inch white cardstock base
5 narrow strips of coordinating paper cut
	to ¾×3 inches each
Coordinating cardstock for Christmas lights
Red/cream bakers' twine
3½×5-inch cardstock for inside greeting
Scoring blade for folding card
Trimmer; scissors
Tracing paper

Corner rounder
Adhesive, including fine-tipped liquid glue
	and dimensional dots
Embossing folder
Round ornament die or punch
Printer or stamps for outside and inside
	greeting

WHAT YOU DO

1. Score and fold white card base in half (completed card measures 4¼×5½ inch). Card opens at bottom. Round corners.

2. Cut and adhere strips of paper to front of card. (Tip: Start with the center strip, then adhere the two outside strips, then finally the two strips next to the center strip.)

3. For Christmas lights, trace pattern, *below,* onto tracing paper. Trace onto colored cardstock; emboss. Cut tops from white cardstock. Adhere a white top to each light bulb.

4. Adhere the light bulbs to the front of the card, some with pop dots. Thread twine through the holes in the tops of the light bulbs. Arrange as desired, then secure ends of twine with tiny dots of liquid glue. Allow to dry. Print or stamp greeting and adhere to inside of card.

Christmas Lights
Full-Size Pattern

divine
desserts

'TIS THE SEASON TO SPLURGE! Whether you're celebrating holiday meals with immediate family or inviting friends to join you for an evening around a dessert buffet, this seasonal extravaganza of sweet endings is sure to impress. Even familiar standbys—like pecan pie—can be tweaked to create something new and unexpected. You'll find these hard to resist!

SIMPLY DAZZLING! Guests will long remember standout desserts like **Cranberry Tart,** *opposite,* where crimson cranberries and custard fill a flaky phyllo crust. Another unbeatable treat is ice cream-filled **Chocolate-Raspberry Yule Log,** *above left,* which has marzipan berries and leaves for its festive garnish. The golden **Apple-Pear Tart,** *above right,* features a cookie crumb crust and luscious caramel topping. **Cranberry and Orange Strudel,** *below left,* showcases tender, rich phyllo swirled around a warmly spiced cranberry-apple filling. Recipes begin on page 135.

SPECTACULAR SHOWPIECES. What could be more elegant than garnishing Lemon-Berry Ribbon Torte, *below right,* with sugar-coated berries and thyme? Even silky-smooth Pumpkin Crème Caramel custards, *above left,* are striking with pomegranate seeds glistening on top. Decadent Chocolate Mixed Nut Tart, *opposite,* stands out with simple drizzles of melted chocolate. Hazelnut Pavlova with Coffee Cream, *below left,* is a work of art with layers of crisp, hazelnut-studded meringue, satiny cream, and chocolate. Recipes begin on page 134.

Lemon-Berry Ribbon Torte

Shown on page 132

WHAT YOU NEED

3   eggs
1½ cups all-purpose flour
1½ teaspoons baking powder
1½ cups granulated sugar
¾   cup milk
3   tablespoons butter
     Powdered sugar
1   8-ounce carton sour cream
1   cup whipping cream
¾   cup powdered sugar
1   teaspoon vanilla
⅔   cup purchased lemon curd
⅔   cup raspberry preserves
     Small fresh lemon thyme or thyme sprigs (optional)
     Fresh raspberries (optional)

WHAT YOU DO

1. Allow eggs to stand at room temperature for 30 minutes. Meanwhile, grease the bottom of a 15×10×1-inch baking pan; line with waxed paper. Grease and flour the waxed paper and sides of pan; set aside. In a small bowl stir together flour and baking powder; set aside.
2. Preheat oven to 350°F. In a large bowl beat eggs with an electric mixer on high about 4 minutes or until thick. Gradually add granulated sugar, beating on medium for 4 to 5 minutes or until light and fluffy. Add the flour mixture; beat on low to medium just until combined.
3. In a small saucepan combine milk and butter; heat and stir until butter melts. Add milk mixture to egg-flour mixture; beat until combined. Pour batter into the prepared pan.

4. Bake for 20 to 25 minutes or until cake springs back when lightly touched. Immediately loosen edges of cake from pan; turn out onto a clean kitchen towel sprinkled with powdered sugar. Remove waxed paper. Cool completely. Cut cake crosswise into thirds; set aside.
5. For the sour cream frosting, in a large bowl combine sour cream, whipping cream, the ¾ cup powdered sugar, and the vanilla. Beat with an electric mixer on medium until mixture thickens and holds stiff peaks. Place about 1 cup of the frosting into a pastry bag fitted with a small star tip.
6. To assemble dessert, place one of the cake layers on a serving plate. Spread with lemon curd. Top with another cake layer; spread with raspberry preserves. Top with remaining cake layer. Frost top and sides of cake with remaining frosting. Pipe a border around edges of cake. Cover and chill for 2 to 4 hours before serving.
7. Place thyme sprigs in a pie plate; dust with powdered sugar. Place raspberries on a plate; dust with powdered sugar. Garnish cake with sugared thyme sprigs and raspberries. Makes 12 servings.

Decadent Chocolate-Mixed Nut Tart

Shown on page 133

WHAT YOU NEED

     Butter Pastry
4   eggs
1¼ cups light-color corn syrup
¾   cup sugar
¼   cup unsalted butter, melted
1   teaspoon vanilla
     Dash salt
1¼ cups salted mixed nuts
1   cup miniature semisweet chocolate pieces
1   tablespoon shortening
     Sweetened Whipped Cream (optional)

WHAT YOU DO

1. Preheat oven to 350°F. On a lightly floured surface, roll chilled Butter Pastry from center to edges into a circle about 13 inches in diameter. Line a 9×2-inch round fluted deep tart pan that has a removable bottom with the pastry circle. Trim pastry even with top edge of pan.
2. In a large bowl beat eggs with a whisk. Whisk in corn syrup, sugar, butter, vanilla, and salt. Stir in the nuts and ½ cup of the chocolate pieces. Pour filling into the pastry-lined tart pan. Place tart pan in a foil-lined shallow baking pan. To prevent overbrowning, cover tart edge with foil.
3. Bake tart for 25 minutes. Remove foil. Bake for 35 to 40 minutes more or until center seems set when gently shaken. Cool for 1 to 2 hours on a wire rack.
4. Just before serving, in a small saucepan combine the remaining ½ cup chocolate pieces and the shortening. Cook over low heat, stirring constantly, until melted. Cool slightly.
5. To serve, remove side of tart pan. Carefully cut tart into wedges; transfer to dessert plates. Transfer melted chocolate to a clean, small heavy plastic bag; seal bag. Snip a small hole in one corner of the bag; drizzle melted chocolate mixture over tart wedges. If desired, top each serving with Sweetened Whipped Cream. Makes 10 to 12 servings.

Butter Pastry: In a medium bowl combine 1½ cups all-purpose flour, 2 tablespoons sugar, ½ teaspoon baking powder, and ⅛ teaspoon salt. Using a pastry blender, cut in ¼ cup cold unsalted butter until pieces are pea size. In a small bowl beat together 1 egg and 1 tablespoon ice water with a fork. Add egg mixture to flour mixture, stirring with a fork just until moistened. Using your fingers, gently knead the mixture just until it forms a ball. (If dough won't form a ball, add another 1 tablespoon ice water, a little at a time.) Don't overmix; the dough should feel slightly sticky. Use your hands to slightly flatten dough into a disk about 6 inches in diameter. Wrap the disk in plastic wrap and chill in the refrigerator for 45 minutes to 1 hour or until dough is firm and easy to handle.

Sweetened Whipped Cream: In a large chilled mixing bowl combine 1 cup whipping cream, 2 tablespoons sugar, and ½ teaspoon vanilla. Beat with chilled beaters of an electric mixer on medium until soft peaks form (tips curl).

Pumpkin Crème Caramel

Shown on page 132

WHAT YOU NEED

⅔ cup sugar
6 eggs
1 15-ounce can pumpkin
2 5-ounce cans evaporated milk
  (1⅓ cups total)
½ cup sugar
2 teaspoons finely shredded
  orange peel
2 teaspoons vanilla
1½ teaspoons pumpkin pie spice
  Pomegranate seeds (optional)

WHAT YOU DO

1. Preheat oven to 325°F.
2. To caramelize sugar, in a heavy large skillet melt the ⅔ cup sugar over medium-high heat, shaking the skillet occasionally to heat sugar evenly. When the sugar starts to melt, reduce heat to low. Cook, stirring frequently with a wooden spoon, until sugar is golden brown. Remove skillet from heat; immediately pour the caramelized sugar into eight ungreased 6-ounce custard cups. Holding cups with pot holders, quickly tilt to evenly coat bottoms of cups. Place cups in two 2-quart square baking dishes or a large roasting pan.
3. In a large bowl beat eggs until combined. If desired, strain eggs; return strained eggs to a large bowl. Stir pumpkin, evaporated milk, the ½ cup sugar, the orange peel, vanilla, and pumpkin pie spice into eggs. Pour the pumpkin mixture over caramelized sugar in cups. Place the baking dishes or roasting pan on the oven rack. Pour boiling water into the baking dishes or pan around cups to a depth of 1 inch.
4. Bake for 40 to 45 minutes or until a knife inserted near the centers comes out clean. Remove cups from water. Cool

slightly on wire rack. Cover and chill for 4 to 24 hours.
5. To serve, loosen edges of custards with a knife, slipping the point of a knife down the sides to let in air. Invert a dessert plate over each custard; turn cup and plate over together. Scrape the caramelized sugar that remains in the cup onto the custard. If desired, garnish with pomegranate seeds. Makes 8 servings.

Chocolate-Raspberry Yule Log

Shown on page 131

WHAT YOU NEED

4 eggs
⅓ cup all-purpose flour
¼ cup unsweetened cocoa powder
1 teaspoon baking powder
¼ teaspoon salt
½ teaspoon vanilla
⅓ cup granulated sugar
½ cup granulated sugar
  Sifted powdered sugar
1 teaspoon raspberry liqueur
  (optional)
¾ cup seedless raspberry preserves
1 French vanilla ice cream
  Rich Chocolate Frosting
  Purchased marzipan (optional)
  Red decorative sugar (optional)

WHAT YOU DO

1. Separate eggs. Allow egg whites and egg yolks to stand at room temperature for 30 minutes.
2. Preheat oven to 375°F. Grease a 15×10×1-inch jelly-roll pan; line with waxed paper. Grease and flour the waxed paper; set pan aside.
 3. In a small bowl stir together flour, cocoa powder, baking powder, and salt; set aside.
4. In a medium mixing bowl combine egg

yolks and vanilla. Beat with an electric mixer on high about 5 minutes or until thick and lemon color. Gradually add the ⅓ cup granulated sugar, beating on high until sugar is almost dissolved.
5. Thoroughly wash the beaters. In a large bowl beat egg whites with an electric mixer on medium until soft peaks form (tips curl). Gradually add the ½ cup granulated sugar, beating until stiff peaks form (tips stand straight). Fold egg yolk mixture into beaten egg whites. Sprinkle flour mixture over egg mixture; fold in gently just until combined. Spread batter evenly in the prepared pan.
6. Bake for 12 to 15 minutes or until cake springs back when lightly touched. Immediately loosen edges of cake from pan and turn cake out onto a clean kitchen towel sprinkled with powdered sugar. Remove the waxed paper. Roll up towel and cake into a spiral, starting from one of the cake's short sides. Cool on a wire rack.
7. Unroll cake and remove towel. If desired, stir raspberry liqueur into raspberry preserves. In a chilled large bowl stir ice cream with a wooden spoon just until softened enough to spread. Spread ice cream on cake to within 1 inch of the edges. Spread raspberry preserves on ice cream to within 1 inch of edges. Roll up cake and wrap in foil. Freeze for 6 hours.
8. Spread Rich Chocolate Frosting over cake roll. Using the tines of a fork, score the frosting lengthwise so it resembles tree bark. Cover and freeze for at least 2 hours or up to 1 week.
9. Let stand at room temperature for 10 minutes before serving. If desired, shape marzipan into holly leaves and holly berries; roll berries in red decorative sugar. Garnish log with marzipan berries and leaves. Makes 10 servings.

Rich Chocolate Frosting: In a heavy, small saucepan combine 3 ounces unsweetened chocolate and 3 tablespoons butter. Heat and stir over low heat until chocolate melts. Remove from heat. Add 1½ cups sifted powdered sugar and ¼ cup milk, stirring until smooth. Add 1½ cups sifted powdered sugar; stir in enough additional milk (1 to 2 tablespoons) to make spreading consistency. Spread immediately over cake roll.

Cranberry and Orange Strudel

Shown on page 131

WHAT YOU NEED

1½ cups cranberries
2   cups peeled, cored, and chopped tart
     apple (about 2 large)
1   cup packed brown sugar
1   tablespoon water
1   teaspoon finely shredded
     orange peel
½   teaspoon ground cinnamon
1   3-inch sprig fresh rosemary
¼   cup finely chopped pecans
16   sheets frozen phyllo dough
     (14×9-inch rectangles), thawed
½   cup butter, melted
     Powdered sugar (optional)

WHAT YOU DO

1. In a heavy medium saucepan combine cranberries, apples, brown sugar, the water, orange peel, cinnamon, and rosemary. Cook and stir over medium heat about 15 minutes or until liquid is slightly thickened (mixture will get juicy as it cooks). Remove the rosemary; stir in pecans. Cover and chill for 2 hours or until completely cooled.
2. Preheat oven to 425°F. Line a baking sheet with parchment paper; set aside. Place 1 sheet of phyllo on a clean work surface. (As you work, keep the remaining phyllo dough covered with plastic wrap to prevent it from drying out.) Lightly brush phyllo dough with some of the melted butter. Top with another phyllo sheet and brush with butter. Repeat layering, using 8 sheets of phyllo total. Spoon half the cranberry mixture on top of the stacked sheets, leaving a 1-inch border on the two short sides and one of the long sides and a 2-inch border on the other long side. Fold the short sides in 1 inch over the filling. Roll up the phyllo and filling, starting from the long side with the 1-inch border. Seal seam by pressing together with

fingers. Place the strudel, seam side down, on the prepared baking sheet. Repeat with remaining phyllo sheets, butter, and filling to make a second strudel. Brush the tops and sides of the strudels with remaining melted butter.
3. Bake for 15 to 18 minutes or until browned. Carefully transfer strudel to serving plate. Cool 15 minutes. If desired, sprinkle with powdered sugar. Slice with a serrated knife and serve warm or at room temperature. Makes 12 servings.

Cranberry Tart

Shown on page 130

WHAT YOU NEED

1   cup fresh cranberries
¼   cup sugar
1   tablespoon orange juice
1   8-ounce package cream cheese
⅓   cup sugar
1   egg
1   egg white
1   teaspoon vanilla
     Butter-flavor nonstick spray
6   sheets frozen phyllo dough
     (14×9-inch rectangles), thawed
1   ounce white chocolate baking
     square (with cocoa butter), melted
     (optional)

WHAT YOU DO

1. Preheat oven to 350°F. In a small saucepan combine cranberries, the ¼ cup sugar, and the orange juice. Cook over medium heat until the cranberries pop and the mixture thickens slightly, stirring frequently. Set aside.
2. In a medium mixing bowl combine cream cheese, the ⅓ cup sugar, the egg, egg white, and vanilla; beat with an electric mixer on medium until well mixed, scraping sides of bowl as necessary. Set aside.
3. Coat a 9-inch tart pan or pie plate with nonstick spray. Unfold phyllo dough; remove 1 sheet of the phyllo dough.

(As you work, cover the remaining phyllo dough with plastic wrap to prevent it from drying out.) Coat the phyllo sheet with nonstick spray. Fold the phyllo sheet in half crosswise to form a rectangle (9×7 inches). Gently press the folded sheet of phyllo into the prepared tart pan, allowing ends to extend over edge of pan. Coat with nonstick spray. Coat and fold another sheet of the phyllo; place across first sheet in a crisscross fashion. Coat with nonstick spray. Repeat with remaining phyllo sheets. Bake for 5 minutes.
4. Spoon cream cheese mixture into phyllo crust, spreading evenly. Spoon cranberry mixture over cream cheese mixture. Using a knife, gently swirl to marble mixture slightly.
5. Bake for 20 to 25 minutes or until phyllo is lightly browned and filling is set. Let cool on a wire rack for 1 hour. Cover and chill for 2 to 4 hours before serving. If desired, drizzle edges of phyllo with melted white chocolate. Makes 10 servings.

Apple-Pear Tart

Shown on page 131

WHAT YOU NEED

10   pecan shortbread cookies, crushed
     (1⅓ cups)
½   cup all-purpose flour
¼   cup butter, melted
1   ounce cream cheese, softened
1   egg
¼   cup caramel ice cream topping
2   firm ripe pears, peeled, cored, and
     cut into 12 wedges each
2   apples, cored and cut into 12 wedges
     each (do not peel)
2   tablespoons butter
1   tablespoon lemon juice
2   tablespoons caramel ice cream
     topping

WHAT YOU DO

1. Preheat oven to 350°F. In a bowl combine crushed shortbread cookies, flour, and ¼ cup melted butter. Pat mixture into bottom and up sides of 14×5×1-inch rectangular or 10-inch round tart pan with removable bottom. Bake crust 10 minutes. Set aside.

2. In a medium bowl beat cream cheese with electric mixer on medium high for 30 seconds. Add egg and ¼ cup caramel ice cream topping; beat until smooth. Spread mixture in bottom of baked crust. Bake 10 minutes more or until center appears set when pan is shaken. Cool on wire rack. Cover and chill at least 2 hours or up to 24 hours.

3. In a 12-inch skillet cook pears and apples in 2 tablespoons butter over medium heat 10 minutes or until tender but still holding their shape, stirring occasionally. Add lemon juice; heat through. Spoon fruit mixture into tart. Drizzle with 2 tablespoons caramel topping. Pass any extra fruit that doesn't fit into tart. Makes 8 servings.

Peppermint Brownie Pie
Shown on page 129

WHAT YOU NEED
½ cup butter
3 ounces unsweetened chocolate, chopped
Pastry for a Single-Crust Pie
3 eggs, lightly beaten
1½ cups sugar
½ cup all-purpose flour
1 teaspoon vanilla
1 cup mint-flavor semisweet chocolate pieces
Whipped cream

WHAT YOU DO
1. In a small saucepan combine butter and chocolate. Cook and stir over low heat until melted; cool slightly.

2. Meanwhile, preheat oven to 350°F. Prepare Pastry for a Single-Crust Pie. On

a lightly floured surface, slightly flatten dough. Roll dough from center to edge into a 12-inch circle. Wrap pastry circle around rolling pin; unroll into a 9-inch pie plate. Ease pastry into pie plate without stretching it. Trim pastry to ½ inch beyond edge of pie plate. Fold under extra pastry even with edge of plate. Crimp edge as desired. Do not prick pastry.

3. For filling, in a large bowl combine eggs, sugar, flour, and vanilla. Stir in melted chocolate and the chocolate pieces. Pour filling into the pastry-lined pie plate.

4. Bake about 55 minutes or until filling is evenly puffed and edge is slightly cracked. Cool on a wire rack about 20 minutes (center will sink slightly as pie cools). Top each serving with whipped cream and, if desired, garnish with chocolate mint candy curls and peppermint candies. Makes 8 servings.

Pastry for a Single-Crust Pie: In a medium bowl stir together 1½ cups all-purpose flour and ½ teaspoon salt. Using a pastry blender, cut in ¼ cup shortening and ¼ cup butter, cut up, or shortening until pieces are pea size. Sprinkle 1 tablespoon ice water over part of the flour mixture; toss gently with a fork. Push moistened dough to side of bowl. Repeat with additional ice water, 1 tablespoon at a time (¼ to ⅓ cup total), until all of the flour mixture is moistened. Gather mixture into a ball, kneading gently until it holds together.

Hazelnut Pavlova with Coffee Cream
Shown on page 132

WHAT YOU NEED
4 egg whites
1 teaspoon vanilla
¼ teaspoon cream of tartar
1⅓ cups sugar
1 cup coarsely chopped hazelnuts (filberts)
3 ounces semisweet chocolate

3 tablespoons butter, softened
1 3-ounce package cream cheese, softened
⅓ cup sugar
1 cup whipping cream
3 tablespoons coffee liqueur
Coarsely chopped hazelnuts (filberts) (optional)

WHAT YOU DO
1. Allow egg whites to stand at room temperature for 30 minutes. Draw two 8-inch circles on a foil-lined baking sheet; set aside.

2. In a large bowl combine egg whites, vanilla, and cream of tartar. Beat egg white mixture with an electric mixer on medium until soft peaks form (tips curl). Gradually add the 1⅓ cups sugar, a tablespoon at a time, beating on high about 7 minutes or until stiff peaks form (tips stand straight) and sugar is almost dissolved. Gently fold in ¾ cup of the 1 cup nuts.

3. Spread half of the egg white mixture over each circle on the baking sheet. Sprinkle the remaining ¼ cup nuts over the top of one of the rounds. Bake for 35 minutes. Turn off oven. Let meringues dry in oven, with door closed, for 1 hour.

4. Just before assembling, in a small saucepan combine chocolate and 1 tablespoon of the butter. Cook and stir over low heat until melted. Set aside to cool. In a medium mixing bowl combine the remaining 2 tablespoons butter and the cream cheese; beat with an electric mixer on medium until smooth. Beat in the ⅓ cup sugar. Gradually add whipping cream, beating on low until combined, then beating on medium just until soft peaks form. Stir in coffee liqueur.

5. Carefully peel meringues from foil. Place the meringue without nuts on a serving plate. Drizzle with some of the chocolate mixture. Chill about 15 minutes or until chocolate is set. Spread with whipped cream mixture. Place second meringue on top, nut side up. Drizzle with the remaining chocolate mixture. If desired, sprinkle with additional chopped nuts. Cover loosely and chill for 2 to 24 hours before serving. To cut, dip knife into hot water before each slice. Makes 12 servings.

fun, fresh, and festive

WHETHER YOU LOVE TO CREATE wreaths, stitch aprons, or sew Christmas stockings—make them even more fun this year by choosing colors with a happy holiday twist. Hot pink stars, apple green ruffles, and golden yellow doilies make the season happy and bright.

BRIGHT STAR BOXES Turn ho-hum gift boxes into Bright Star Boxes by adding a colorful star on the top. Then add other embellishments to make your holiday package really shine. Instructions are on page 145.

VINTAGE POM-POM WREATH Combine bright pom-poms with vintage accents to make a Vintage Pom-Pom Wreath, *above left*, to brighten your holiday this year. The wreath is quickly designed by choosing colors of similar intensity and starting with a purchased foam wreath. Instructions are on page 145.

DOILY DRESS-UP PACKAGES Vintage doilies and a little adhesive spray make it easy to create Doily Dress-Up Packages, *above right*. Tie the boxes with twine for a simple, homespun look. Instructions are on page 146.

HAPPY HOLIDAY SHOPPING BAG Get in the spirit of the season by sewing a bright Happy Holiday Shopping Bag, *above*, using Christmas print fabrics in fresh colors and patterns. The bag has pockets inside and out for holding those special Christmas treasures. Jumbo rickrack adds just the right holiday trim. Instructions are on page 145.

POLKA-DOT TABLE RUNNER Set your
holiday table in style with a Polka-Dot
Table Runner, *above*, that is pieced using
bright colors of fabric. Choose a pattern
and solid colors that match the theme of
your Christmas decorating. Instructions
are on page 147.

POLKA-DOT STOCKING Make a matching
Polka-Dot Stocking, *opposite*, to hang for
Santa this Christmas. The little polka-
dots are slightly stuffed to give
dimension. Instructions are on page 145.

SWEET CANDY JARS Perfect for a last-
minute table decoration or a quick gift,
Sweet Candy Jars, *left*, will be loved by
any age! Instructions are on page 146.

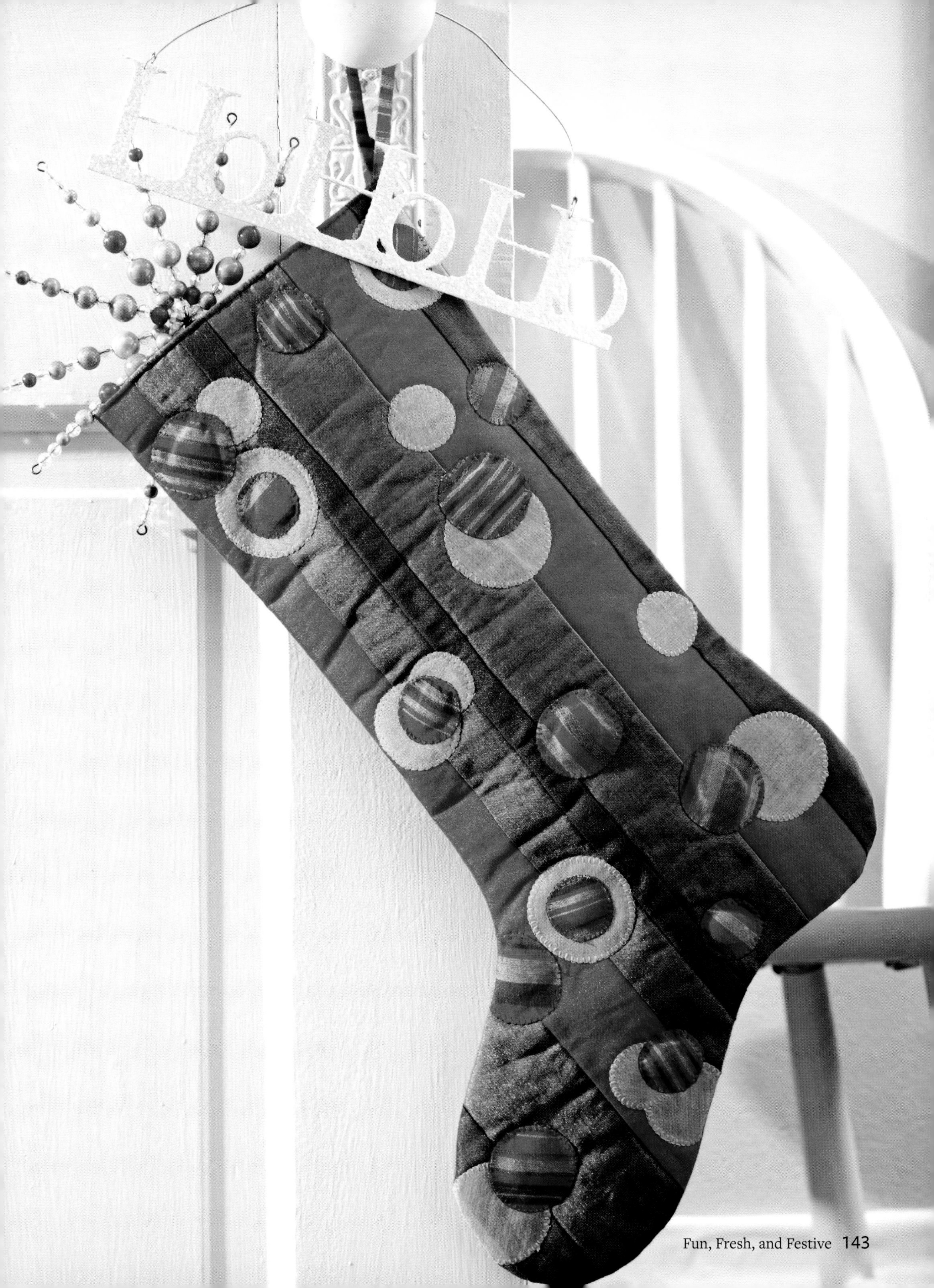

FESTIVE RUFFLED APRONS Big girls and little girls alike will love to wear Festive Ruffled Aprons that you make using favorite fabrics in red and green. The main part of the aprons can be made with solid or print fabric, and the ruffles upon ruffles are gathered using printed fabrics. A patch pocket holds special little treats or a miniature rolling pin for the little ones. Instructions begin on page 148.

Bright Star Boxes

Shown on page 139

WHAT YOU NEED

Tracing paper
Pencil
Bright colors of cardstock
Patterned scrapbook papers
Scissors
Colored twine, alphabet letter stickers, and desired embellishments

WHAT YOU DO

1. Choose a purchased box to be decorated. Enlarge and trace the star pattern, *below*.

2. Cut out the stars from different colors of cardstock. **Note:** If you want, scrapbooking stores have die-cutting systems that you can use to quickly cut multiple shapes.

3. Once you have the shapes cut out, dress up the sides of the boxes with a variety of holiday-patterned papers. Add a glittered chipboard initial or create a custom name tag using a punched circle matted with a scalloped-edge cardstock circle. Tie your tag creations onto the box tops using twine or gingham ribbon.

Package Topper
Enlarge 150%

Vintage Pom Pom Wreath

Shown on page 140

WHAT YOU NEED

Plastic foam wreath form with flat back
Craft pom-poms (and/or yarn and a pom-pom maker)
Hot-glue gun and glue sticks
Vintage light reflectors
Scissors
Embellishments, such as felted balls, vintage light reflectors, cupcake liners, tree bulbs

WHAT YOU DO

1. Make pom-poms in various colors and sizes, if you're creating your own.

2. Lay the supplies on the form to get an idea of the layout. Strive for visual balance and full coverage.

3. Use the hot-glue gun to affix the embellishments. You could use just about anything you can find in bulk: bulbs, pinecones, vintage buttons, cupcake liners, recyclables.

Happy Holiday Shopping Bag

Shown on page 141

WHAT YOU NEED

½ yard cotton print fabric for the body of the bag (cut to 38×18 inches)
1⅛ yards heavy-weight iron-on interfacing for the body of the bag (cut to 38×18 inches)
¼ yard cotton fabric to back outside pockets (cut two pieces to 18×8 inches)
Assorted cotton print fabrics for outside pockets (two cut to 9½×8 inches and four cut to 4¾×8 inches)
½ yard print fabric for inside lining (cut to 36×18 inches)

One 10×6-inch piece cotton fabric for lining of inside pocket
1 yard hot pink 1½-inch-wide rickrack
⅔ yard 1-inch-wide webbing
3⅔ yards ¾-inch-wide grosgrain decorative ribbon
9-inch zipper
Matching sewing threads
Marking pen

WHAT YOU DO

1. Iron interfacing to back of fabric for outside body of bag. Using ¼-inch seam, stitch three outside pocket pieces together along the 8-inch sides, with largest pocket in the center. Piece other section of three pockets together in the same manner. With right sides together, stitch outside pocket lining to joined pockets, using ¼-inch seam, stitching along both long 18-inch edges. Turn right side out and press. Place rickrack along top edge of both pocket sections, extending rickrack over top of pocket sections. Using matching sewing thread, stitch through center of rickrack to attach to the top of the pocket sections.

2. Lay main part of the bag flat and mark 5½ inches from each short (18-inch) end. Place rickrack-topped edge of the pocket pieces along the markings, having bottom of pocket sections toward center of bag main body piece. Pin pocket sections in place. Sew close to the bottom edges of the pocket sections to attach to bag body piece. Baste the side edges of the pocket sections to long edges of the main part of the bag. Fold the main part of the bag in half with wrong sides together, lining pockets up. Gently press the center fold line to use in placing the straps.

3. For webbing handles, place decorative ribbon in the center and sew close to the edges of the ribbon, through the webbing. Fold webbing in half and mark the halfway point. Lay the main part of the bag flat and

measure 4½ inches in from each long 38-inch edge. Starting at the center pressed line, lay the strap parallel to the 38-inch edge with the edge of the webbing at the 4½-inch markings (this will be at the seam of the outside pockets, extending onto the center pocket sections). Stop 2½ inches from the 18-inch edge of the main body section when pinning straps onto bag. Keep strap straight and bring the halfway mark of the strap over to the fold line on the bag on the other side. Continue pinning strap to bag, bringing the end of the strap to where the strap started, butting ends together. Place the edges of the straps on the 4½-inch markings from the long edge, stopping 2½ inches from the ends of the fabric. Sew along edge of straps, stopping and pivoting at the 2½-inch markings, sewing across the ends, sewing the edges, pivoting again at the top edge and returning to the start. Repeat for the second strap.

4. With right sides of the bag together, match pockets at side edges and sew side seams using ½-inch seam allowance. Press seams open. Fold bag so side seam is directly over the bottom fold line on the bottom of the bag. Measure 2 inches up from the point that was formed and stitch a perpendicular line across the side seam at the 2-inch mark. Trim off the triangle, leaving ½-inch seam allowance.

5. On the lining, measure 3½-inches down from one short 18-inch side and draw a 9-inch line in the center of the fabric. Draw a line ¼ inch from the first line on both sides of the original line. Square lines at the end to make a rectangle. Using short sewing machine stitches, sew along the rectangle lines, pivoting at the corners. Cut the center line, clipping diagonally to the corners to form triangles. Press the slit sections to the wrong side along the stitching lines.

6. Center the zipper in the opening on the wrong side of the fabric. Stitch zipper in place, sewing close to pressed edges of the rectangle opening. Place the 10×6-inch piece of inside pocket lining fabric on the wrong side of the lining behind the zipper. Top edge of the pocket piece should be just above the top zipper tape. Pin fabric in place and stitch edge of pocket through lining. Sew a second row of stitching just inside the first row for extra strength.

7. With right sides together, fold the long edges of the lining together and sew side seams using ½-inch seam allowance. Sew the squared bottom corners the same way as for the body of the bag and press. With the main bag right sides out and lining inside out, insert main bag inside the right side of the lining. Match side seams and lining edges to edges of bag. Sew lining and bag together, leaving an opening to turn bag right side out. Turn bag right side out, pushing lining into the inside of the bag. Press top edge of bag and topstitch around top of bag to close opening used for turning.

Doily Dress-Up Packages
Shown on page 140

WHAT YOU NEED
Package to be wrapped
Doilies in bright colors
Adhesive spray
String or twine

WHAT YOU DO
Choose colors from the same color palette for the package wraps and doilies. Use adhesive spray to adhere to the front of the package. Tie with twine.

Sweet Candy Jars
Shown on page 142

WHAT YOU NEED
FOR THE CANDY STICKS JAR
Empty glass jar
Square piece of Christmas-print fabric about 12×12 inches
Rubber band
Ribbon
Jingle bell
Scissors
Colorful candy sticks

FOR THE LOLLIPOP JAR
Glass jar
Red candies
Lollipops
Ribbon

WHAT YOU DO
For the Candy Sticks Jar

Be sure the jar is clean and dry. Lay the fabric on a table and place the jar in the center of the fabric. Pull the fabric up and around the jar. **Note:** If the fabric seems too big for the jar, cut to a smaller square size. Place the rubber band around the fabric to hold in place. Slide the jingle bell on the ribbon and tie around the jar. Place candy sticks in the jar.

For the Lollipop Jar

Be sure the jar is clean and dry. Fill the jar with candy. Place the lollipops in the candy. Tie bows around the jar and the lollipops.

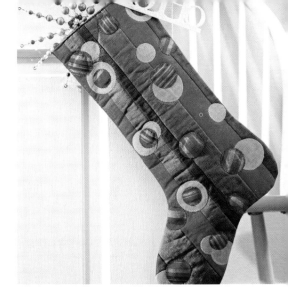

2. Cut 12 squares of fabric 3½×3½ inches from different striped fabrics (Piece C)

3. For sashings, cut two 1½×9½-inch strips (Piece D), two strips 1½×17½ inches (Piece E), and four strips 1½×3½-inches (Piece F).

4. For binding, cut 2⅓-inch strips to equal about 78 inches total length.

WHAT YOU DO

1. Use ¼-inch seam allowances throughout. Sew D to opposite sides of A. Sew three C blocks together, four times. Sew one set of CCC to either side of AD. Stitch E pieces to both sides of ADCCC. Sew together two units of BFCCCFB and join to either side of center unit.

2. Use scraps of fabrics to piece together a backing to measure 19×19 inches. Layer top, batting, and backing; baste together and quilt as desired, or leave unquilted.

3. Trace three circle sizes onto fusible webbing paper. Iron onto desired fabrics and cut-out shapes. Arrange on top of quilt top. Fuse in place only the shapes to lie underneath other overlapping circles and ones you wish to lie flat. Pin other overlapping circles on top of other circles to determine overall look desired.

4. Buttonhole Stitch around flat shapes using matching threads. For striped circle shapes, place a small ball of cotton or polyfil underneath circle and fuse lightly around outside edges. Buttonhole Stitch around outside edges. With wrong sides of long edges together fold binding strip in half and iron flat. With right sides together, sew binding strip in half and iron flat. With

right sides together, sew binding strip to outside edge of quilt top, fold to the back and tack in place.

Polka-Dot Table Runner

Shown on page 142

WHAT YOU NEED

Tracing paper
Pencil
Scissors
¼ yard each red, green, purple, and yellow cotton fabrics
⅓ yard striped cotton fabric for lining
Matching threads
Small pieces polyfil or cotton balls
Fusible webbing
20×20-inch square of thin cotton batting

WHAT YOU DO

Refer to the diagram, below, and cut the following:

1. From desired fabrics, cut one square 9½×9½-inches (Piece A) and four squares 3½×3½-inches (Piece B).

Polka-Dot Stocking

Shown on page 142

WHAT YOU NEED

Tracing paper
Pencil; scissors
¼ yard each red, green, purple, and yellow cotton fabrics
⅓ yard striped cotton fabric for lining
Matching threads
⅓ yard thin quilt batting
Small pieces polyfil or cotton balls
Fusible webbing

Polka-Dot Table Runner
Placement Diagram

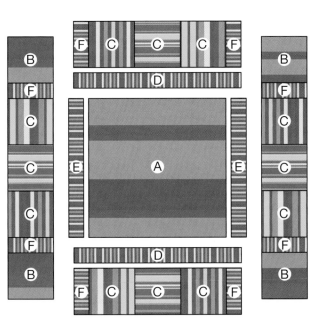

Polka-Dot Table Runner
Assembly Diagram

WHAT YOU DO

1. Enlarge and trace the stocking pattern, *right*. Cut two stocking pattern pieces from lining fabric. Set aside. Cut 18-inch long strips of solid fabrics varying widths ranging from 1 to 2½ inches wide. Piece together solid fabrics to make a 18×24-inch piece of fabric. Cut two stocking patterns from this pieced fabric. Cut two stocking patterns from batting and baste to both stocking pieces.

For the Circle Embellishments

1. Trace circle patterns onto fusible webbing. Iron onto back of striped and yellow fabrics. Cut out circles along lines. Arrange as desired on striped pieced stocking pieces, overlapping some circles and leaving others separate. Iron down all yellow circle shapes and buttonhole stitch around edges using matching thread. Place striped dots where desired. Before ironing striped dots to stocking, insert a small balled up piece of polyfil or piece of cotton ball underneath striped circle shapes to give them more dimension. Lightly iron around outside edges. Buttonhole-stitch around outside edges.

2. With right sides together, sew stocking pieces together using ¼-inch seam allowance. Clip curves, turn, and press lightly. With right sides together, sew lining pieces together. Clip curves. Iron top edges of stocking ½ inch to the inside and iron top edge of lining ½ inch to the outside. Insert lining inside the stocking. Make a hanging loop by cutting a 2×9-inch piece of striped fabric. With right sides together, stitch long edges together using a

Polka-Dot Stocking
Enlarge 400%
Cut 2 from fabric, reversing 1
Cut 2 from lining, reversing 1

¼-inch seam. Turn right side out and press. Insert loop at top right side of stocking between outside and lining fabrics. Baste together close to top folds. Stitch lining and stocking together by stitching close to top fold, also stitching through loop at side edge.

Festive Ruffled Aprons
Shown on page 144

For Adult Apron

WHAT YOU NEED
Marking pen
Tracing paper
⅞ yard red medium weight-cotton fabric (twill or duck cloth) for apron body
Two pieces of cotton print fabric, 2¾×22 inches for waist ties
One piece of cotton print fabric, 2¾×25 inches for neck strap
One 9×9-inch piece cotton print fabric for pocket
Two 6×74-inch strips of print fabric for lower ruffles
One 4×74-inch strip of print fabric for lower ruffle
Matching sewing threads

For Child Apron (4–6 Size)

WHAT YOU NEED
Marking pen
Tracing paper
⅜ yard cotton print fabric for apron body
6×6-inch piece of cotton fabric for pocket
Three 2½×18-inch pieces of cotton print fabric for waist ties and neck strap
Two or three 3×44-inch pieces cotton print fabric for bottom ruffles
One 5×44-inch piece cotton print fabric for bottom ruffle (if a little extra length is desired, use a 5-inch ruffle at bottom with two 3-inch ruffles above)
Matching sewing threads
Scrap of floral fabric to cut motif for pocket
Scrap of fusible webbing

WHAT YOU DO
1. For adult or child apron, follow the same directions, with exceptions noted. Enlarge and trace patterns, *opposite*. Cut out pieces from desired fabric. Turn ¼ inch to the wrong side along cut edge of armhole. Turn again ¼ inch and stitch close to folded edge. Fold neck strap in half lengthwise, right sides together. Stitch in a ⅜-inch seam. Turn right side out and press.

2. With right sides together, pin ends of strap to upper edge of apron, adjusting length of neck strap as desired. Baste 1 inch from cut edge of apron, through ends of neck strap. Turn upper edge to wrong side so cut edge just meets stitching and press. Turn again to wrong side along stitching line and press. Stitch close to folded edge.

3. Fold tie ends in half lengthwise with right sides together. Stitch long edges and one end in ⅜-inch seam. Clip corners, turn, and press. Pin tie ends to apron at the top of the side seam. Baste 1 inch from cut

edges, through tie ends. Turn back edge to wrong side until cut edge just meets stitching and press. Turn to back again along stitching line and press. Stitch along folded edge. Hem bottom edge the same as the side edges.

4. Narrowly hem long ends of all ruffles by folding under ¼ inch twice to the wrong side and stitching close to the fold. Fold under short ends of ruffles in the same way and hem. Baste down center of ruffles and pull up thread to gather. Pin bottom ruffle to lower edge of apron, with wrong side of ruffle to right side of apron front. Sew over center gathering line to attach ruffle to apron. Gather remaining ruffles in the same manner and pin in place just above the lower ruffle. Stitch down centers through apron.

5. Stitch around outside edge of adult pocket ½ inch from side and lower edges. Press seam allowance to the back of the pocket. Fold the top of the adult pocket 1 inch to the back twice, press, and stitch close to folded edge. For child's pocket, stitch around side and lower edges ¼ inch and press to the back along stitching line. Fold top down ¼ inch, press, and stitch close to folded edge. Pin adult pocket 2 inches and child's pocket 1½ inches from the top center of the apron front. Stitch close to side and lower edges to attach to apron. A floral motif may be fused to center of pocket and stitched on before attaching to apron if desired.

Adult Ruffled Apron
Enlarge 400%
Cut 1

Place on fold

**Child Ruffled
Apron Pocket**
Enlarge 400%
Cut 1

Child Ruffled Apron
Enlarge 400%
Cut 1

Place on fold

**Adult Ruffled
Apron Pocket**
Enlarge 400%
Cut 1

watch the season
glow

CANDLES ARE BURNING, lights are twinkling, and stars are all aglow. Celebrate the season by creating your own shimmering centerpieces, festive displays, and winter welcomes that shine with the spirit of the season.

CRANBERRY AND CANDLES CENTERPIECE
Red and green votive candles are tucked into
fresh cranberries to make a Cranberry and
Candles Centerpiece. The candles are
purchased already in the glass container and
lined up on a long tray. Greenery and a dusting
of coarse sugar give the centerpiece sparkle.
Instructions are on page 157.

ART CANDLES Simple candles become works of art when you carve them using a linoleum cutter. Create Art Candles, *below left*, in all kinds of shapes and sizes carving in favorite Christmas motifs. Instructions are on page 157.

CONFETTI POPCORN ARRANGEMENT Pure white candles are surrounded by colorful popcorn to make a Confetti Popcorn Arrangement, *below right*. Use as a fun holiday centerpiece. Instructions are on page 157.

CHARMED CANDLES Little pieces of scrapbook papers combine with ribbons and charms to make Charmed Candles, *above left*. Group these simple-to-make candles on a tray to make an equally charming centerpiece. Instructions are on page 157.

HAPPY STICKERS CANDLES Miniature stickers dot a purchased candleholder to create Happy Sticker Candles, *above right*. Surround the candles with gold jingle bells to make a quick centerpiece. Instructions are on page 158.

GLOWING GLOBE DISPLAY A gazing ball becomes the center of attention in a Glowing Globe Display, *below*, that can be put together in minutes. The greenery that surrounds it is a fresh evergreen wreath with tiny light tucked inside—all resting on a black birdbath. Instructions are on page 158.

SPARKLING CHRISTMAS GRAFITTI BOOTS Spell out your holiday messages on Sparkling Christmas Grafitti Boots, *opposite*, that you make in minutes. Simply write the holiday messages and designs using a permanent metallic marker and then add twinkling stem lights inside the boots. Instructions are on page 158.

TREE LIGHTS CANDLE Add a little light around your candle with some Christmas tree light bulbs in bright holiday colors. Make the Tree Lights Candle in the colors that fit your holiday color scheme. Instructions are on page 158.

HOLIDAY SAND CANDLES Layers of brightly colored sand surround simple pillar candles to create Holiday Sand Candles. Instructions are on page 158.

Cranberry and Candles Centerpiece

Shown on page 151

WHAT YOU NEED
Small votive candles in glass jars
Large rectangular tray
Fresh cranberries
Fresh greenery
Coarse sugar

WHAT YOU DO
Set the candles on the tray. Pour fresh berries around the candles. Add greenery. Dust with sugar.

Art Candles

Shown on page 152

WHAT YOU NEED
Pillar candle in desired color
Pencil
Linoleum cutter tool
Rectangular white plate
Clear glass round plate
Greenery

WHAT YOU DO
Mark the desired design on the candle using the pencil. Use the linoleum cutter to carefully cut the design into the candle.

Set the candle on the rectangular plate and then on the round plate. Surround with greenery.

Confetti Popcorn Arrangement

Shown on page 152

WHAT YOU NEED
White plate or tray
White pillar candles
Confetti popcorn

WHAT YOU DO
Place the candles on the tray. Surround with confetti popcorn.

Charmed Candles

Shown on page 153

WHAT YOU NEED
Purchased candles in desired colors
Scrapbook paper scraps in coordinating colors
Ribbon scraps
Purchased charm
Straight pins

WHAT YOU DO
Cut small pieces of scrapbook paper and pin to the candle. Wrap the ribbon around the candle crossing in the front. Pin a charm where the ribbon crosses. Add other ribbons to candle if desired.

Never leave a burning candle unattended.

Happy Stickers Candles

Shown on page 153

WHAT YOU NEED
Votive candles in glass containers
Small Christmas-motif stickers
Clear glass plate
Gold jingle bells

WHAT YOU DO
Be sure the glass on the votive candles is clean and dry. Adhere the stickers on the glass. Place on the glass plate. Surround with jingle bells.

Glowing Globe Display

Shown on page 154

WHAT YOU NEED
Fresh evergreen wreath
Red gazing ball
Double-stick tape
One-piece birdbath
Red and white Christmas lights
Pinecones and shiny Christmas balls
    (optional)

WHAT YOU DO
Set the evergreen wreath in the center of the birdbath. Place the gazing ball in the center of the wreath. Secure with double stick tape if necessary. Tuck the lights into the wreath. Add pinecones and shiny Christmas balls if desired.

Sparkling Christmas Grafitti Boots

Shown on page 155

WHAT YOU NEED
Pair of rubber boots
Permanent metallic markers
Twinkling stem lights
Glittered artificial greenery

WHAT YOU DO
Be sure the boots are clean and dry. Write messages and draw Christmas designs on the boots as desired. Let dry. Arrange the stem lights and glittered greens in the boots.

Tree Lights Candle

Shown on page 156

WHAT YOU NEED
Pillar candle in desired color
Christmas tree light bulbs in desired
    colors
Glass plates

WHAT YOU DO
Place the candle in the center of the stacked plates. Surround the candle with the tree lights.

Holiday Sand Candles

Shown on page 156

WHAT YOU NEED
Pillar candle in desired color
Clear glass container
Sand in a variety of colors

WHAT YOU DO
Be sure the container is clean and dry. Place the candle in the center of the clear glass container. Surround the candle with the colored sand, layering the colors as you pour.

Never leave a burning candle unattended.

Stitch Diagrams

Backstitch

Chain Stitch

French Knot

Running Stitch

Star Stitch

Stem Stitch

Straight Stitch

Knitting Abbreviations

approx	approximately
beg	begin(ning)(s)
cn	cable needle
dec	decrease(s)(ing)
dpn(s)	double-pointed needle(s)
end	ending
est	established
inc	increase(s)(ing)
inc 1	increase 1 (knit into the front and back of the next stitch)
k or K	knit
k2tog	knit two stitches together (right-slanting decrease when right side facing)
p or P	purl
p2tog	purl two stitches together (right-slanting decrease when right side facing)
pat	pattern
pwise	as if to purl
rem	remain(s)(ing)
rep	repeat(s)(ing)
rev	reverse
rnd(s)	round(s)
RS	right side(s) of work
sl	slip
sl1-k	slip next stitch as if to knit

sl1-p	slip next stitch as if to purl
sm	slip marker
ssk	(slip, slip, knit) slip two stitches, one at a time knitwise, insert left needle and knit two together (left-slanting decrease when right side facing)
st(s)	stitch(es)
St st	stockinette stitch (knit RS rows, purl WS rows)
tbl	through the back loop(s)
tog	together
WS	wrong side(s) of work
yo	yarn over
yon	yarn over needle
yrn	yarn around needle
[ ]	work step in brackets the number of times indicated
( )	work instructions within parentheses in the place directed and the number of times indicated
*	repeat the instructions following the single asterisk as directed

Tips for Felting Wool

Felting wool fabric brings the fibers in the wool closer together and gives it a more compact look and feel. The texture becomes more irregular and interesting. Always choose 100% wool fabric to felt. Sweaters that are nearly 100% wool will work, but the fibers will not be as tight. Sweaters that have less than 90% wool will not work well.

Place the wool inside an old pillowcase to prevent any tiny fibers from washing out. Then wash the wool in very hot water with a little laundry detergent. Agitation of the wool loosens fibers and helps to shrink the wool. Dry the wool in a hot dryer to shrink the maximum amount.

Press the wool with a press cloth if desired. Tightly felted wool does not ravel, and edges and seams can usually be left raw or unfinished, similar to purchased felt.

Sources

To purchase a large-sized, sleek and stylish reindeer from *Wood Magazine* visit:
woodstore.net/
sleekstylrei.html

Felt
National Nonwovens
nationalnonwovens.com

General Crafting Supplies
Hobby Lobby
hobbylobby.com

Michaels Arts & Crafts
michaels.com
1-800-michaels

Needle-Felting Supplies
decadentfibers.com

Paper/Scrapbooking Supplies
American Craft
americancrafts.com

Bazzill
bazzillbasics.com

Vintage Cards and Stickers

The Gifted Line
johngrossmanline.com

Craft Designers

Rita Anderson 55
Susan Banker 113
Heidi Boyd 14, 43, 45, 58, 61, 62, 96
Susan Cage 63
Carol Dahlstrom 48, 59, 60, 78, 79, 94, 106, 110, 113, 142, 151, 152, 153, 154, 155
Phyllis Dobbs 106
Jackie Dickie 55
Allisa Jacobs 97
Katie LaPorte 76, 77
Stephanie Lynn 47
Janet Petersma 56, 57, 80, 81, 89, 92, 93, 94, 114, 115
Pamela Porter 49
Ann E. Smith 109
Jan Temeyer 7, 8, 9, 75, 78, 79, 97, 105, 107, 108, 111, 112, 141, 142, 143, 144
Danielle Thompson 140
Mary Tucciarone 103

Index